TOWER BRIDGE

HISTORY ○ ENGINEERING ○ DESIGN

KENNETH POWELL

Thames & Hudson

CONTENTS

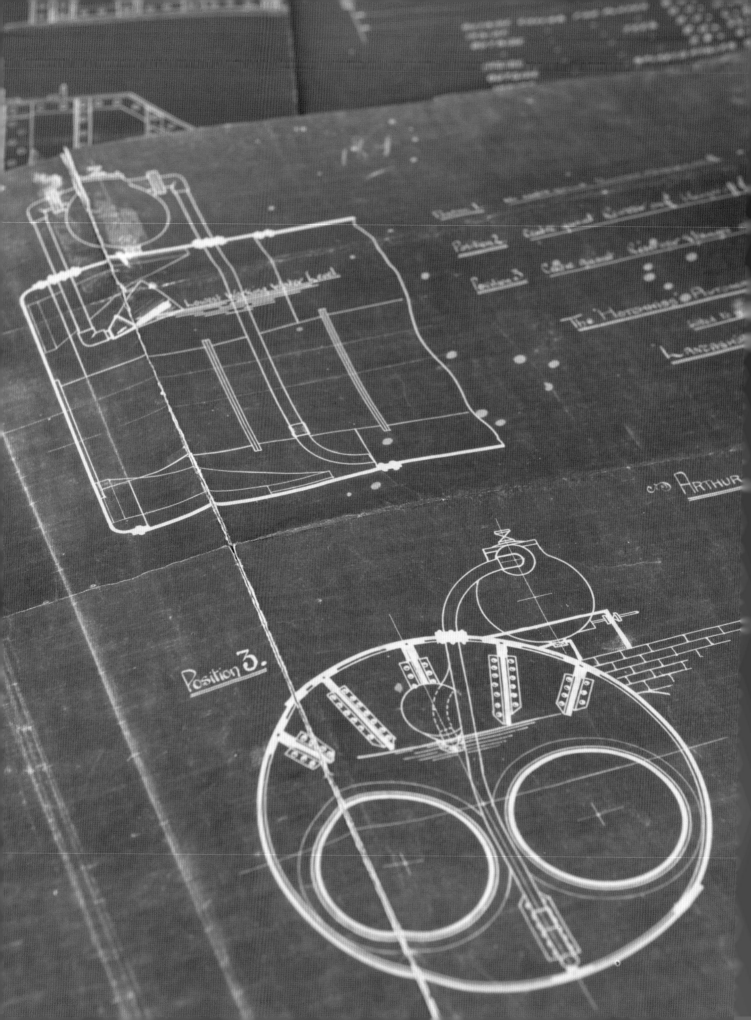

Position 3.

ARTHUR

TOWER BRIDGE   CONTRACT Nº 7

Elevation of Main Towers facing Opening Span.
Scale 8 feet to an Inch.

CONTRACT DRAWING Nº 301

shown to the undersigned at the time of his
executing a certain Contract, bearing date the
2ᵈ day of July _____ 1889, and made
between the undersigned of the one part and The
Mayor and Commonalty and Citizens of the City
of London of the other part, and referred to in
the said Contract.

Perry & Co

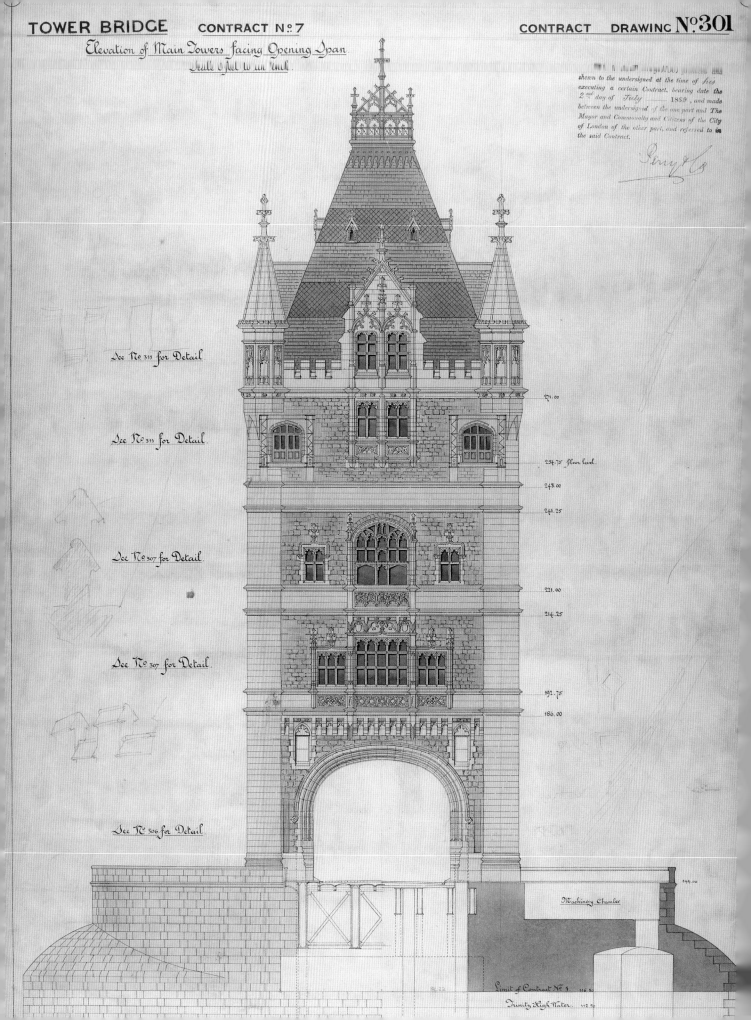

See Nº 311 for Detail.

See Nº 311 for Detail.

See Nº 307 for Detail.

See Nº 307 for Detail.

See Nº 306 for Detail.

271.00

254.75 floor level.

248.00

241.25

221.00

214.25

192.75

186.00

144.00

Machinery Chamber

Limit of Contract Nº 1

Trinity High Water. 112.50

ARCHITECTURE — OR ENGINEERING? Or an awkward fusion of both? Purists may quibble: one Victorian critic damned the 'ridiculous departure from faith and truth' that resulted from clothing a massive steel structure in masonry.[1] But after its completion in 1894 Tower Bridge quickly became a potent image of London. This it remains, alongside Big Ben at the Houses of Parliament, St Paul's Cathedral, and more recent landmarks such as the Gherkin (30 St Mary Axe) in the City of London, the Shard at London Bridge and the London Eye on the South Bank.

BELOW
Panoramic aerial view of
London in 1831 by Robert
Havell, looking west along
the Thames.

Since opening to the public in 1982, Tower Bridge has become a popular tourist attraction. It features in countless photographs taken by visitors to London over the last 125 years – most of them captured today on mobile phones. Tower Bridge is a comparative parvenu amongst the bridges of central London. It was the last to be constructed before the opening of the pedestrian-only Millennium Bridge linking Bankside with the City in 2000. Until the completion in 1991 of the Dartford Crossing linking Kent and Essex, it was the last Thames bridge before the sea.

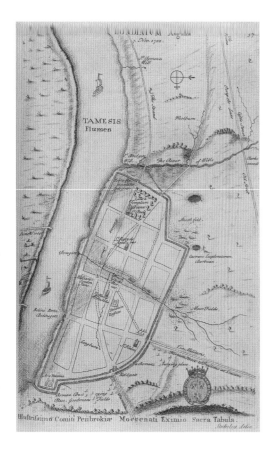

Since Roman times the river Thames has been a fundamental element in the identity of London. For nearly 2,000 years, it was the great artery that underpinned the capital's trading economy. Archaeologists have confirmed that there was a Roman bridge on the site of the present London Bridge, initially a simple timber pontoon structure built for military use. This was destroyed in the revolt of Boudicca, queen of the Iceni tribe of Britons, against the occupying Roman forces in AD 60–61, when the Roman city of Londinium was razed and most of its inhabitants slaughtered.

The bridge was rebuilt in a more permanent form, but still of timber, as part of a major development of Londinium's waterfront in the second half of the first century AD. The Roman bridge probably survived the centuries of London's post-Roman decline, patched up and partially rebuilt, until, in 1091, a catastrophic flood brought about its total collapse. Quickly reconstructed, it was destroyed by fire in 1136.

So in 1176 work began on a new bridge of stone. This was one of the wonders of the medieval world, and was designed by a talented priest, Peter of Colechurch. Twenty arches carried the roadway linking the City of London with the growing suburb of Southwark, the City's backyard on the south side of the river. Peter of Colechurch died a few years before the completion of the bridge in 1209 and was buried beneath the first structure to be erected on it: a chapel dedicated to the great London saint Thomas Becket. It was always intended that

Ee nouuelles dalbyon
Il vous en plaist escouter
Mon frere & mon cõpaignõ
Lehez qua mon retõmer
Ay este deca la mer
Et eu a iolxuse chiere

London Bridge, like Florence's Ponte Vecchio, should carry houses and shops. Their rents, along with tolls on those crossing, funded its upkeep.

From 1282 onwards the maintenance of London Bridge was entrusted by royal charter to the Bridge House Estates. As a committee of the Corporation of the City of London, this body remains responsible for the present London Bridge and four other Thames bridges, including Tower Bridge. Maintaining the bridge was always a major responsibility, subject as it was to 'the forces of natural decay, coupled with the continual danger caused by the violent impact of river and tide'.[2] Fire posed another threat – more than once houses on the bridge were burned down, though it escaped with only minor damage in the Great Fire of 1666.

The medieval London Bridge familiar to Geoffrey Chaucer and William Shakespeare incorporated a drawbridge that could be raised to allow small vessels to pass beneath. But in effect the bridge marked the termination of the Port of London. The Pool of London downstream was the hub of London's maritime trade, where the Thames was filled with a myriad of masts, and lined with wharves and warehouses on both banks. The development of enclosed dock complexes from the beginning of the nineteenth century – the first to open was West India Docks on the Isle of Dogs in 1802 – ensured London's position as a great world port in the age of the Industrial Revolution.

BELOW
Lead plaque with the mark of the Bridge House Estates. It would have been displayed on property owned by the Estates.

BOTTOM
William Daniell's view (1803) of the newly constructed London Docks at Wapping, looking north.

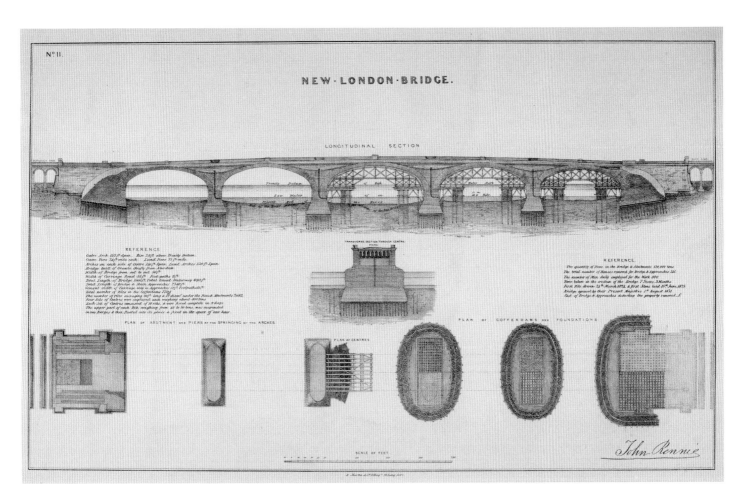

ABOVE

Sections and plans of
abutments, centres,
cofferdams and foundations
for the new London Bridge,
designed by John Rennie
and completed in 1831.

The old London Bridge was finally replaced by a fine new stone
structure. Designed by John Rennie (1761–1821) and constructed under
the direction of his son John (1794–1874), it was opened in 1831 by
King William IV. 'Many snuff boxes and other memorials' were made
from the timber houses and shops of the old bridge.[3] Rennie's bridge,
in turn, was demolished in the 1960s, and a replacement opened in 1973.
The nineteenth-century bridge was sold for £1 million to Robert P.
McCulloch, an oil magnate who was planning to develop a new holiday
resort on Lake Havasu in Arizona, USA. The stones were carefully
numbered and transported across the Atlantic, with re-erection of
the bridge at Lake Havasu City completed in 1971. (The legend that
McCulloch thought that he was buying Tower Bridge has no substance
– he was photographed sitting proudly on London Bridge shortly after
the sale agreement had been signed.)

By the end of the nineteenth century a series of new bridges had been constructed across the Thames. A timber bridge built at Putney in 1729 was replaced by a masonry structure in the 1880s. In central London, Westminster Bridge was opened in 1750, Blackfriars Bridge (for road and foot traffic) in 1769, Waterloo Bridge in 1817, and Southwark Bridge in 1819 – all were subsequently rebuilt at least once. In addition, during the 1860s, railway bridges spanned the Thames to serve Blackfriars, Cannon Street and Charing Cross stations.

The river was no longer the barrier it had been for many centuries. Despite the creation of new crossings, London Bridge remained the principal gateway to the City from the south. It was, a report to the Bridge House Estates Committee in 1871 explained,

the only roadway across the Thames for the great population which lies to the east of it on both sides of the river. If a straight line be drawn five miles [8 km] to the north and five miles to the south of this bridge there will be found for the most part to the east of it thirty-seven important Metropolitan districts which in 1861 had a population of 949,000 and probably now have quite a million or about one third of the entire Metropolitan population.[4]

Horse-drawn vehicles had to compete for space with a flood of people travelling over London Bridge on foot, many coming and going from the sprawling railway station on the south side. There were suggestions that this bridge should be widened – this improvement took place, though not until the first decade of the twentieth century. Increasingly a new river crossing downstream was seen as the solution to the chronic congestion. 'A new bridge lower down the river, with suitable approaches, will alone relieve it effectually and meet the present and future needs of the population', the Bridge House Estates Committee resolved.[5] This project, it argued, was 'the most pressing Metropolitan improvement'.[6]

Between 1851 and 1901 London more than doubled in size and population. The transformation of Paris masterminded by Baron Haussmann was driven by the edict of the French Emperor Napoleon III. A more cautious and piecemeal approach to 'metropolitan improvement' prevailed in Britain, with its constitutional monarchy and fervent attachment to free enterprise. It took a series of cholera outbreaks to make the creation of an effective sewer system a priority. (More than 14,000 Londoners died during the epidemic of 1848–49 and another 10,000 in 1853.) Designed by Joseph Bazalgette (1819–91), a Londoner from a Huguenot (French Protestant) family and then Engineer to the Metropolitan Commission of Sewers, it served London well for a century and a half. From 1856 Bazalgette acted as

ABOVE
Portrait of Sir Joseph Bazalgette, 1863. His greatest achievement as an engineer was the creation of London's sewer system.

BELOW
A late 19th-century photograph of the Thames below London Bridge, showing the river crowded with barges and ships.

Dockers loading the
steamship *Arawa* in the
Royal Albert Dock, *c.* 1885.
The dock, the second of
the 'Royals' in east London,
was completed in 1880.

View of the Upper Pool of
the Thames in the 1880s.
Watermen, who carried
passengers along and
across the river, ply for
trade opposite the Tower
of London.

Chief Engineer of the Metropolitan Board of Works. Set up in 1853, this was the first truly London-wide authority and was responsible for the embankments along the Thames as well as new thoroughfares such as Shaftesbury Avenue and Northumberland Avenue. When the idea of a new bridge east of the Pool of London moved towards realization, Bazalgette, along with other less distinguished designers, was to enter the fray with a series of proposals. The Board of Works also sought to assert its own potential role in the project. But in the end the City, which had effectively controlled the river crossings since medieval times, was the agent for progress, creating the landmark of London that is Tower Bridge.

2 | BRIDGING THE THAMES

LONDON BRIDGE

THE RIVER THAMES has been central to the history of London since Roman times. It is a highway, the gateway to a wider world, but equally a barrier dividing the city. By the mid-1870s the population of the area of London east of London Bridge, on both sides of the Thames, was more than one million. (By 1881 metropolitan London contained more than four million people.) It was 'on one side as large as Liverpool, and on the other side as large as Manchester, Salford, and Birmingham combined', a Parliamentary select committee was told in 1884.[1] For centuries London Bridge was the sole crossing point on this stretch of the river for vehicles. The only alternative for pedestrians was to use one of the many small ferry boats that had been the traditional means of travel along the Thames for many centuries. A steam-powered ferry between Wapping on the north side of the river and Rotherhithe on the south side opened in 1877. It did not prove commercially viable, however, and closed nine years later.

OPPOSITE, TOP
Map of London from *Civitates Orbis Terrarum* by Georg Braun and Franz Hogenberg (1572). This was the first town plan of the city and shows London Bridge as the principal river crossing.

OPPOSITE, BOTTOM
Watercolour of old London Bridge, with watermen ferrying passengers across the river. From the 'Album Amicorum' of Michael van Meer, c. 1614–15.

The first London Bridge had been constructed by the Romans. Located immediately south of the Forum, the social and commercial focus of the Roman city, it was the end point of all the main road routes converging on London. Its medieval successor, patched and mended, survived into the first decades of the nineteenth century. Under the terms of an Act of Parliament passed in 1756, most of the houses that lined the bridge were removed in 1758 under the supervision of George Dance the Elder (1695–1768) as Clerk of the Works, an ancient City office. An arch 70 ft (21 m) wide was inserted into the centre to enable the passage of ships. But, by the end of the eighteenth century, 'the nuisance of so defective and crazy a structure over a great navigable river like the Thames became so intolerable that the good citizens of London were at length compelled to abandon this historic relic and form plans for the erection of another and more suitable structure in its stead'.[2]

An unrealized proposal of 1800 by George Dance the Younger (1741–1825), then Clerk of the Works in succession to his father, and Surveyor of the Bridge House Estates, provided for the replacement of London Bridge by two new bridges, 100 yds (91 m) apart. Each had opening drawbridges. This formed part of an ambitious scheme of urban reconstruction worthy of Paris but unachievable in London. In this city the interests of private property would have been paramount, ruling out the extensive clearances needed. A magnificent design, published in 1801, was produced by the engineer Thomas Telford (1757–1834) for a single-span iron bridge. It would have provided 65 ft (20 m) of clearance for ships at high water, but equally remained unbuilt. Both these proposals would have allowed ships to pass upstream of London Bridge, with the potential for new wharves to be developed up to Blackfriars. The old London Bridge – by the early decades of the nineteenth century an extraordinary, if inconvenient, survival – was finally replaced by John Rennie's bridge in 1831. But by the 1880s even that bridge was proving woefully inadequate for the needs of what had become a global metropolis. The development from 1836 onwards of London Bridge railway station, on the south side of the river, added greatly to the pressures on the bridge. There 250,000 commuters arrived daily, most of whom were bound for the City on the north side.

THE GRAND SUSPENSION BRIDGE
OVER THE THAMES,
BELOW LONDON BRIDGE.

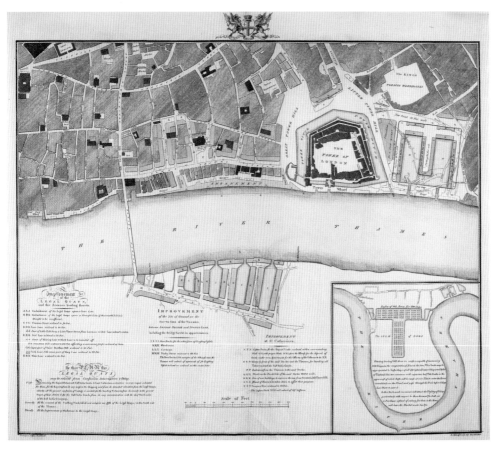

THE POOL OF LONDON

The Scottish engineers Samuel Brown (1776–1852) and James Walker (1781–1862) had produced designs for a suspension bridge immediately east of the Tower of London in 1824. They proposed to raise the funds needed (£392,000) on the money markets but investors were not found. Much of the debate surrounding the project for a new river crossing, which eventually became Tower Bridge, centred on the role of the Pool of London. Adjacent to the heart of the City, the Pool encompassed 'legal quays' and 'sufferance wharves' on both banks of the Thames. These were the only legally authorized places for landing goods in London. By the end of the eighteenth century over 10,000 coasters and 3,500 larger ships were coming to London annually. The larger vessels had to anchor downriver from the Pool, as far as Greenwich about 6 miles (9.6 km away). From there thousands of lighters (large barges) ferried goods to the wharves in the City and Southwark. (Lighterage – the transfer of cargo between barges and larger ships – remained fundamental to the trade of London well into the twentieth century.) The system allowed for extensive pilfering and consequently led to the formation of the Thames River Police, the world's first organized police force.

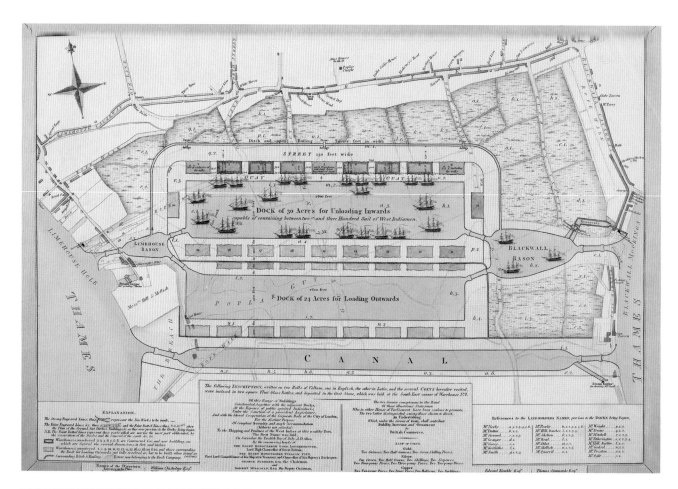

TOP

Plan of West India Docks,
1801. To the south of the
docks is shown the City
Canal. This proved a failure
and was later converted
into the South Dock.

ABOVE

Grand Panorama of London
by Charles Evans, 1849.

The solution to these issues was the construction of enclosed docks, east of the City, surrounded by walls, heavily policed and containing large warehouses for storing goods. The first such complex was the West India Docks, constructed in 1802–6 on the Isle of Dogs, followed soon after by the East India and London Docks. The St Katharine Docks, adjacent to the Tower of London, opened in 1828. Engineered by Thomas Telford, their building required the demolition of a dense area of slum housing, along with the medieval Hospital of St Katharine. In due course, railways provided an important means of transporting goods from the docks directly to any point in the United Kingdom.

But the Pool of London remained in active use by ships and lighters. Hay's Dock, close to London Bridge, for example, was developed in the 1850s and was a major point for the import of foodstuffs – the first consignment of New Zealand butter arrived there in 1867. (The Hay's Wharf Company eventually owned most of the wharves on the south side of the river from London Bridge to Tower Bridge, and was still building new cold stores after the Second World War.) The big warehouses of St Mary Overy's Wharf in Southwark followed in the 1880s – evidence of continuing investment in the Pool. The proprietors and users of the wharves around the Pool were always stoutly defensive of their interests, as the promoters of the new Tower Bridge were to discover.

RIGHT
Watercolour view by
G. Yates of Tooley Street,
Southwark, in 1834. Carts
are being loaded outside
a warehouse on the site
of Hay's Wharf, developed
in the 1850s.

TUNNELS UNDER THE THAMES

In 1843 a new river crossing opened in the form of the Thames Tunnel. Linking Wapping and Rotherhithe, it was the first tunnel under a river in the world. First projected in 1802, the 1200-ft (366-m) long tunnel was completed to designs by Sir Marc Isambard Brunel (1769–1849), assisted by his son, Isambard Kingdom Brunel (1806–59). The Thames Tunnel was a staggering technical achievement but it had taken eighteen years to complete, at ruinous cost. It was intended to carry vehicles as well as pedestrians, recouping its cost from tolls. However, there was no funding to build the ramps for vehicles, so, even with heavy pedestrian traffic, it never became profitable. Briefly a tourist attraction, with shops and cafés, by 1860 it was 'damp stained and peeling', used by vagrants, thieves and prostitutes, and avoided by the respectable.[3] Within twenty years the tunnel was closed, its management having gone bankrupt. It was converted to carry the trains of the East London Railway Company, travelling from the City to the south coast. This railway was later integrated into the London transport system and today it forms part of the London Overground.

BELOW
View of the Thames Tunnel, linking Wapping and Rotherhithe. Opened in 1843 and the first tunnel under a river in the world, it became briefly a fashionable tourist location but was later closed and converted for use by trains – today it carries part of the London Overground.

OPPOSITE
Sir Marc Isambard Brunel, engineer of the Thames Tunnel, painted in 1812–13 by James Northcote.

Tunnelling was always an expensive and risky business. While the Tower Bridge project was in gestation, the Great Western Railway's Severn Tunnel, linking England with south Wales and begun in 1873, was beset by delays. It eventually took thirteen years to complete and the final cost was far above the original estimates, while maintenance was a major ongoing expense. As J. E. Tuit, one of the engineers who oversaw the construction of Tower Bridge, commented: 'the experience that has been gained in the construction of subaqueous tunnels shows that they are to be avoided wherever possible'.[4]

The failure of the Thames Tunnel notwithstanding, the idea of a tunnel as a means of crossing the river did not go away. The Blackwall Tunnel (opened in 1897) and the Rotherhithe Tunnel (completed in 1908), both built by the London County Council, are major routes today. Given the large number of people working in the docks, warehouses and factories close to the Pool of London, there was clearly a case for a pedestrian tunnel in the vicinity. The Tower Subway opened in 1870 between Irongate Stairs off Tower Hill and the picturesquely named Pickle Herring Street on the south bank of the river. It was the brainchild of Peter Barlow (1809–85), Chief Engineer to the South Eastern Railway. The tunnel, 60 ft (18 m) below the riverbed, was constructed using a circular tunnelling shield of cast iron, instead of the square timber shield used by the Brunels. Little more than 7 ft (2 m) high internally, the tunnel was lined not with the brick favoured by the

THE TOWER SUBWAY.

Workers constructing the
Tower Subway, using the
cast-iron shield designed
by J. H. Greathead. Opened
in 1870, the subway under
the river remained in
use until 1894, when the
opening of Tower Bridge
made it redundant.

BOTTOM
View along the Tower
Subway, showing the rails
that originally carried the
passenger carriages.

OPPOSITE, TOP
The engineer John
Henry Greathead, who
collaborated with Peter
Barlow on the construction
of the Tower Subway. The
Greathead shield that he
developed was also used
in the construction of the
City and South London
Railway, the world's first
underground electric
railway and now part
of the Northern Line.

OPPOSITE, BOTTOM
Passengers in one of the
cable-drawn carriages on
the Tower Subway, from
the *Illustrated London
News*, 1870. Within a year,
the subway was converted
to a pedestrian walkway.

Brunels but with prefabricated segments of cast iron. For a price of two pence (first class) or one penny (second class) passengers were conveyed under the river in a fourteen-seat cable-drawn carriage.

The system had its drawbacks – passengers had to use lifts at either end of the tunnel and wait underground for an available seat. Within the year the subway was converted to a pedestrian walkway. Although a grim means of crossing the river – unlit, damp and with restricted space – it continued in use until it became redundant with the opening of Tower Bridge in 1894. Barlow campaigned against the bridge project, publishing a pamphlet in 1878, *The Tower Bridge: observations to prove that a new bridge east of London Bridge is unnecessary*. Undeterred by the failure of the Tower Subway, he secured backing for a tunnel extending from the City to Elephant and Castle in south London. It was completed under the supervision of the brilliant South African engineer J. H. Greathead (1844–96), who had worked with Barlow on the Tower Subway. This tunnel became the route for the City and South London Railway, opened in 1890 and later part of the Northern Line, the first of London's 'tubes'.

SUBMISSIONS FOR THE SPECIAL BRIDGE
OR SUBWAY COMMITTEE

The pressure for a new river crossing east of London Bridge, as well as the widening of the latter to deal with perennial traffic jams, was growing. However, it was unclear whether the project should be the responsibility of the City of London Corporation or of the Metropolitan Board of Works. In 1872 a bill providing for a 'tower bridge' was submitted to Parliament but the matter languished until 1876. In that year a string of petitions presented to the City Corporation led to the establishment of a 'Special Bridge or Subway Committee'. The committee decided in favour of a new bridge or subway close to the Tower of London rather than the widening of London Bridge. Ideas were invited, and came in from a number of contenders, some of whom were well-established engineers. It does not appear that a formal competition was launched and no premiums were paid. Only one of the submissions, by a Mr John Keith, provided for a tunnel – 'a sub-riverian arcade', as he described it – on the scale of the later Rotherhithe and Blackwall tunnels and costed at over £500,000.

Most of the remaining proposals were for bridges, which had to allow for the passage of ships into the Pool of London. Should a bridge be a low-level structure, with a provision for an opening section, or so high that ships could simply pass beneath it? If the latter, major works

BELOW
The tunnel entrance to John Keith's 1876 proposal for a 'sub-riverian arcade' beneath the Thames. It anticipated in scale the later Blackwall and Rotherhithe tunnels.

OPPOSITE, TOP
George Barclay Bruce's 1876 design for a 'rolling bridge' across the Thames.

OPPOSITE, BOTTOM
Frederic Barnett's 1876 design for a proposed duplex bridge. It was claimed that this would allow 'uninterrupted continuity of vehicular and general traffic'.

PROPOSED NEW BRIDGE ACROSS THE THAMES BELOW BRIDGE.

WITHOUT DESECRATING LONDON BRIDGE.
  This Patent Bridge can be built in any part of the Thames.

WITHOUT Depreciating the valuable Wharf Property that covers its shores.

WITHOUT causing the loss of time and wear of Horses and Vehicles, traversing unprofitably daily thousands of miles to reach London Bridge, and return on the opposite shore.

WITHOUT Stopping the Passage of Ships or the Vehicular traffic for a moment. The openings for Ships will be increased according to advised requirements.

PROVISIONAL DESIGN
AND PLAN FOR
PATENT IMPROVED BRIDGE
FACILITATING THE PASSAGE OF LARGE SHIPS WITHOUT
STOPPING THE VEHICULAR AND GENERAL TRAFFIC.

FREDERIC BARNETT
PATENTEE.

would be needed to create elevated approach roads, inevitably involving the acquisition and clearance of many properties. One of the more unusual submissions came from George Barclay Bruce (1821–1908). A distinguished railway engineer and sometime assistant to Robert Stephenson, he proposed a 'rolling bridge'. This consisted of a platform 300 ft (91 m) long and 100 ft (30 m) wide carried on six piers, spaced so as to provide ample passageways for ships, with rollers to propel the platform across the river. About 1,400 foot passengers and 100 vehicles could be accommodated on the platform, which took about three minutes to roll across the Thames. The scheme was ingenious but of dubious practicality (though its promoter 'considered that it solved the question of approaches').[5] As much could be said of Frederic Barnett's proposal. This was for a bridge featuring two road loops with sliding sections that would be drawn back to allow ships to pass, via a sort of lock, while traffic continued on the alternate loop. The difficulties involved in operating such a structure can be imagined.

Over the next few years ideas continued to flow thick and fast. A. J. Sedley's proposal was for a high-level suspension bridge, with a clear span of 750 ft (228 m), providing a barely adequate 85 ft (26 m) of clearance for ships at low water. The scheme wrestled with the ongoing dilemma that any proposal for a high-level bridge faced: how to provide approach roads on the north and south banks at a reasonable gradient for horse-drawn traffic, without massive clearances of buildings on both

BELOW
Peter Barlow and Robert Richardson's 1862 design for a suspension bridge across the Thames on the site of Tower Bridge. Another suspension bridge was proposed by A. J. Sedley in the 1870s.

sides of the river. On the south side of the Thames, Sedley proposed a spiral ramp for vehicles, akin to that in a present-day multistorey car park. The engineer Sidengham Duer (d. 1886) proposed to solve this problem by installing huge lifts at each end of a high-level bridge, so that disruption to adjacent property would be minimal.

Henry Vignoles (1827–99) was an experienced railway engineer who had worked across Europe. He addressed the issue of costly property acquisition by proposing for the south side of the river '…a gigantic warehouse, about 750 ft [228 m] long and 100 ft [30 m] wide, along the sides and ends of which the approach road was to rise to the bridge level by the easy gradient of 1 in 50…. The erection of the warehouse would have, it was believed, recouped to a great extent the cost of land.'[6]

One possible precedent was provided by the hydraulically powered swing bridge across the river Tyne in Newcastle upon Tyne. It replaced a Georgian stone bridge of nine arches, itself superseding a vanished medieval bridge. The swing bridge was completed in 1876 and was engineered by the firm of W. G. Armstrong (see Chapter 4). One driver of the project was Armstrong's own need for seagoing ships to be able to pass upriver to the company's expanding Elswick engineering works. The Bradford-based John P. Drake (1843–1901), whose speciality was the design of textile mills and waterworks, proposed a similar bridge for London, though the Thames traffic was certainly far greater than that on the Tyne. He did not offer an estimated cost of his scheme.

It was almost inevitable that the great civil engineer Sir Joseph Bazalgette (1819–91) would take an interest in the bridge project, with the backing of the Metropolitan Board of Works. His record of achievement in creating an efficient sewer system for London in the mid-nineteenth century could not be ignored (he was knighted in 1875). Bazalgette's 1878 scheme for a high-level bridge was put forward by the Board as a private bill in Parliament. It was rejected, largely on account of a clearance for ships of 65 ft (20 m) at high water being judged inadequate – Bazalgette argued that tall-masted sailing ships could simply lower their topmasts to pass below the bridge – and in spite of his offering three alternative designs, one featuring a spectacular arch to carry the roadway.

To reduce the impact of the approach road on the south side of the river, Bazalgette took up the idea of a spiral ramp. In 1882 he came back with a revised scheme, allowing 85 ft (26 m) clearance at high water. His name was, however, synonymous with the Board of Works, which had appointed him its Chief Engineer. The City Corporation, it seems, wished to maintain control of the bridge project. (Bazalgette was to remain an active bridge builder, being responsible for the new Hammersmith, Putney and Battersea bridges, all completed between 1886 and 1890.) Within a few years Bazalgette and the Board had changed tack and were arguing the case for a tunnel, rather than a bridge. But the days of the Metropolitan Board of Works were numbered. An unelected body and never popular, it was mired in corruption scandals in its last years and in 1888 it was abolished ahead of the creation of the London County Council in 1889.

Fig. 17—DESIGN FOR SINGLE SPAN STEEL ARCH BRIDGE BY SIR JOSEPH BAZALGETTE, 1878

Fig. 15—CANTILEVER BRIDGE DESIGNED BY SIR JOSEPH BAZALGETTE, 1878

Fig. 16—LATTICE GIRDER BRIDGE DESIGNED BY SIR JOSEPH BAZALGETTE, 1878

OTHER RIVER CROSSING SCHEMES
OF THE 1880s

The City of London Special Bridge or Subway Committee's deliberations having produced no conclusions, the debate over the new river crossing continued. In 1883 the London Chamber of Commerce 'announced that it was prepared to exhibit in its Council Rooms any maps, plans, or models of bridges, tunnels, or any other proposed means of communication across the Thames below London Bridge'.[7] Many schemes were submitted. There were still advocates of a tunnel. Messrs Maynard & Cooke's suggestion of a 'high-level' tunnel, located just below the river bed, was certainly innovative. The tunnel was to be prefabricated of wrought-iron plates – like a ship – and sunk into the river, a strategy that would be adopted in later tunnel projects.

Messrs Kinipple & Morris favoured a low-level bridge with a central opening span. To avoid delays to traffic, they proposed that 'by means of shafts down each pier, communication was to be effected with a subway underneath the bed of the river, so that traffic could be continuously maintained when the central span was opened to allow the passage of vessels through the bridge'.[8] Lifts would lower and raise foot passengers and vehicles to and from the subway. These would use hydraulic power, which was to be a key feature of Tower Bridge as it was finally realized. As an alternative to both a bridge and a tunnel, one C. T. Guthrie

BELOW
Two designs for an opening bridge across the Thames: above is that by Messrs Kinipple & Morris, 1884; below is a much earlier proposal dating from 1801 by Samuel Bentham (brother of the philosopher Jeremy Bentham).

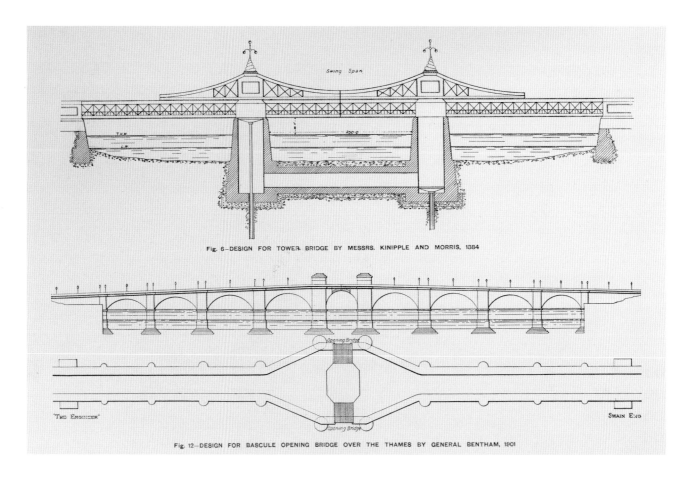

Fig. 6—DESIGN FOR TOWER BRIDGE BY MESSRS. KINIPPLE AND MORRIS, 1884

Fig. 12—DESIGN FOR BASCULE OPENING BRIDGE OVER THE THAMES BY GENERAL BENTHAM, 1801

suggested that a 'steam ford' could be constructed, 'similar to the system
in use at Saint Malo [France]'. Rails would be laid on the riverbed to
carry a steam-driven platform over the water conveying passengers and
vehicles. The potential for conflict with traffic on the river was obvious.

More realistic was the high-level bridge scheme put forward in 1885
by Rowland Mason Ordish (1824–86) and Ewing Matheson (1840–
1917). Matheson was the managing director of the Leeds-based Farnley
Iron Company. Ordish was an accomplished engineer, having advised
on the construction of the train shed at St Pancras Station and the
wrought-iron roof of the Royal Albert Hall. He also worked on
projects in India and the Far East. Perhaps his most celebrated work
was Albert Bridge, linking Chelsea and Battersea and opened in 1873
(though the bridge had to be strengthened a decade later to designs
by Bazalgette). Ordish, moreover, had useful City connections, having
been the engineer for Holborn Viaduct (opened in 1869). In addition,
he was familiar with the site of the proposed bridge, between the Tower
and St Katharine Docks. He had worked on an abortive scheme for a
high-level railway bridge there in 1862–64.

Dismissing the idea of a swing bridge, Ordish and Matheson
proposed a single-span (850-ft [260-m] long) bridge, with no piers in
the river to obstruct traffic. The central portion would be designed to
open using bascules (sections that can be raised and lowered using

counterweights), providing a clearance of 120 ft (37 m) for ships. Pedestrians would be able to cross the bridge even when the central section was open, using a high-level walkway. Looking to a future when ships might cease to use the Pool of London, Ordish and Matheson commented that 'it is not only probable, but almost certain, that in a few years' time the course of trade upon the river, and the inconveniences that must attend even the best kind of opening, will altogether cause the disuse of the moving part of the bridge'.[9] If and when this happened, the bridge could remain permanently closed, and it would therefore be possible to add four lines of railway tracks above the road level. (There was a precedent for such an arrangement in the form of Newcastle's High Level Bridge, completed in 1849.) This proposal was unquestionably forward-looking and far from impractical – in contrast to many of the other schemes put forward – but the City was already set to progress its own proposal for what became Tower Bridge.

EARLY PROPOSALS BY HORACE JONES

In effect the City of London Corporation was the only local authority in London before the establishment of the London County Council in 1889 and the metropolitan borough councils in 1900; most matters of public concern were otherwise dealt with at parish level. As a consequence of its special status, the City had its own architect to handle development projects within its boundaries. (The post of City Architect was established in 1847, replacing the ancient office of Clerk of the Works.) Horace Jones (1819–87) was appointed as City Architect, succeeding J. B. Bunning (1802–63), in 1864. He had spent twenty years in successful private practice. His first major project was a new town hall in the classical style in the then rapidly expanding Welsh port of Cardiff, completed in 1853. His varied workload thereafter had included churches, office buildings in the City, an Oxford Street store for the retailers Marshall & Snelgrove and a country house at Caversham Park in Berkshire. Commissioned by the ironmaster William Crawshay, the house, externally rather dull, featured an innovative use of an iron frame.

Jones's appointment coincided with a push for major improvements in the City of London's infrastructure. He was given the task of rehousing the City's historic markets in state-of-the-art, hygienic new premises. The first section of the new Smithfield Market, the central meat market, was finished in 1867, with further buildings completed between 1873 and 1883. Billingsgate Fish Market followed in 1874–78 and the Leadenhall retail market in 1880–81. Police stations, housing and other City projects fell within his remit. Jones was also responsible for major alterations and additions to the Guildhall, including a spectacular iron-framed council chamber (destroyed by bombing in the Second World War). He was clearly adept at the use of iron, whether exposed or concealed. *The Builder*, a leading professional journal of the time, commented after his death that Jones, while not an 'art architect', had 'a good deal more perception as to the artistic element in architectural

design than would be quite realized by those who knew him only as the architect of the City markets'.[10]

It was probably inevitable that the Tower Bridge project, with the City firmly in charge, would eventually come to Jones, despite the efforts of Bazalgette, Ordish and Matheson, and a number of other, less distinguished contenders. In 1877 he was asked to advise on the various options for a new river crossing close to the Tower. His favoured option was a low-level bridge, which he estimated could be built for about £750,000. A high-level bridge would cost about three times that sum, a tunnel at least twice as much. Addressing the various schemes put forward by Bazalgette, Jones concluded that 'a high level bridge would be a costly and extravagant scheme that if carried sufficiently high to clear all masts, it would be as little used as was the Thames Tunnel'.[11] Bazalgette had costed his proposed bridge of 1882 at £1.25 million, most of that sum being spent on approach roads. Yet Blackfriars Bridge, opened in 1869, had cost no more than £350,000. If the bridge was to be low level, how would it cope with the passage of river traffic?

Putting aside the swing bridge option, Jones proposed in 1878 a bascule (or 'seesaw') bridge (see p. 60). It had a centre span traversed by two hinged steel platforms that would be raised by means of chains from towers. The bascules would be lifted 'by steam power or by hydraulic apparatus, supplied by tanks fixed in the roof of the towers'.[12] Apart from its practical advantages, Jones argued, this solution would

ABOVE
Blackfriars Bridge,
completed in 1869, with
the adjacent Blackfriars
Station.

produce a structure 'capable of architectural treatment…. It might be rendered the most picturesque bridge on the river'.[13] A bascule bridge on this scale was unknown in Britain, though the Hull & Selby Railway (later part of the North Eastern Railway) had constructed one in 1839 to carry its tracks across the river Ouse at Selby in Yorkshire. Operated by manpower, it carried the main railway line from London to York until 1870. It was replaced by a swing bridge in 1889, of which the hydraulic mechanism made by W. G. Armstrong remains in use.

The Special Bridge or Subway Committee endorsed Jones's proposal. However, Charles Welch, the City Librarian, recorded in his meticulous 1894 *History of the Tower Bridge* that 'the report was not adopted and the matter appears to have lapsed for several years'. There was already opposition to the very idea of a bridge in this location, wedged between the Tower of London and St Katharine Docks. A pamphleteer styling himself 'Aquarius' argued that it would destroy the trade of the wharves around the Pool of London and see 'thousands of able-bodied men deprived of their sole source of livelihood in the metropolis'.[14]

In 1880 the Bridge House Estates Committee examined the possibility of an extended free ferry service, funded by the City, as an alternative to a new bridge. A floating chain bridge was another option that the Committee did not rule out. Since 1840 a steam-powered 'floating bridge' had linked Portsmouth and neighbouring Gosport in Hampshire, straddling the entrance to the naval port. (It ceased operating in 1959.)

The City Corporation's motivation was clearly that of economy. So the field remained open for various projects, 'some extremely impracticable in working or costly in execution', to be promoted.[15] The City's prevarication on the matter infuriated businesses operating on either side of the Thames. A petition 'representing every section of the industrial classes in the east and south of London', demanding a new river crossing, was presented to the Court of Common Council, the City's main decision-making body.[16] Gradually, the City moved ahead with Horace Jones's scheme. An impetus came from the deliberations of a House of Commons select committee. It had been considering three privately promoted bills for, respectively, the Metropolitan Board of Works' tunnel project by John Keith, the 'duplex bridge' (a revised version of Palmer's 1877 scheme) and an enhanced ferry service.

Having rejected all these schemes, the select committee concluded that there should be a low-level bridge constructed by the City close to the Tower of London. It finally resolved in July 1884 'that a low-level bridge, with mechanical openings, be erected at Irongate Stairs, at the end of the street known as Little Tower Hill, by the Corporation, out of money to be raised upon the credit of the Bridge House Estates'.[17] The committee urged the City to secure a suitable design and to refer it back to Parliament for approval. 'From January [*sic*] 1884, it may be said

that the question of the *means* of improved communication between
the north and south banks of the lower Thames was settled,' Charles
Welch recorded. 'Subways, duplex bridges and floating bridges sank
into the background, and though the steam ferry was considered
worthy of attention for some time as a palliation of the evil, the low
level bridge was considered as essential.'[18]

The Bridge House Estates Committee was now energized. In the
summer of 1884 a deputation embarked on a tour of the Netherlands
and Belgium. It looked at examples of swing and bascule-operated
bridges, a common feature of the canals in those countries. The swing
bridges in Glasgow, Leith Docks in Edinburgh and Newcastle were
also inspected. The end result was a recommendation for a bascule-
operated bridge on the lines of that suggested by Horace Jones six years
earlier. After years of delay things began to move swiftly. Jones was
instructed by the City in September 1884 'to prepare and submit to
them a design for a low level bridge with mechanical openings'.[19]

'An Act to empower the Corporation of London to construct
a bridge over the river Thames near the Tower of London, with
approaches thereto, and for other purposes' (the 'Tower Bridge Act')

BELOW

Horace Jones's 1878
scheme for an opening
low-level bascule bridge.
The arch proposed over
the central span was
seen as a potential
hazard to shipping. Jones
subsequently collaborated
with John Wolfe Barry on a
revised scheme (bottom),
which included the high-
level walkways that are
a feature of Tower Bridge
as built.

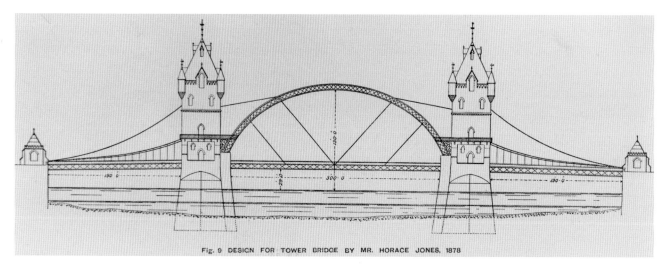

Fig. 9 DESIGN FOR TOWER BRIDGE BY MR. HORACE JONES, 1878

Fig. 10 –DESIGN FOR TOWER BRIDGE, MESSRS. JONES AND BARRY, 1885

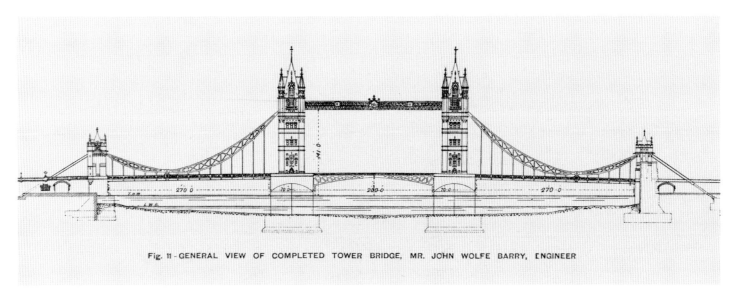

Fig. 11 - GENERAL VIEW OF COMPLETED TOWER BRIDGE, MR. JOHN WOLFE BARRY, ENGINEER

received royal assent on 14 August 1885. The various proposals for 'lifting, sinking, floating and sliding' solutions for crossing the river had been given one final airing as various witnesses were called by the House of Commons select committee. J. H. Greathead argued the case for a subway. Benjamin Baker (1840–1907), codesigner of the Forth Bridge in Scotland, then under construction, strongly endorsed the idea of a lifting low-level bridge.

Rearguard opposition had come from ferrymen and others who feared the bridge would have a detrimental impact on the operations of the riverside wharves. The Southwark & City Riverside Workmen's Committee was vehemently opposed to any new crossing downstream of London Bridge. Thomas Kelly, general secretary of the Amalgamated Society of Riverside Workmen, claimed that 30,000 workers would be 'ruinously affected'.[20] The bridge plan had 'come as a thunderbolt and has created surprise and consternation amongst the vast body of working men dependent on the free navigation of the Upper Pool of the port'. Such objections were to no avail, though there were some provisions for compensation to those adversely affected by the bridge project. The select committee was convinced that the new bridge would be 'an enormous public advantage'. Moreover, it could be provided 'without taxing anybody to the extent of a single halfpenny'.[21] One significant provision of the 1885 Act was the stipulation that the central span should be 200 ft (60 m), rather than the 160 ft (48 m) proposed. This would provide a generous channel for ships entering the Pool, where they moored two abreast.

Horace Jones's 1878 scheme had been, he admitted, 'a very crude notion' that needed to be developed. There was an obvious problem with the great steel arch proposed over the central (lifting) span of the bridge. Tall-masted ships could possibly collide with it unless they kept to the very centre of the river. Architecturally, Jones envisaged a structure clad in minimal Gothic detailing, executed in brick with stone dressings. By the 1890s the Gothic Revival was a declining force in British architecture but the proximity of the proposed bridge to the

OPPOSITE, TOP

An exquisite pen-and-ink
drawing (1884) by Horace
Jones of his design for
Tower Bridge, seen with
the bascules open for the
passage of ships.

OPPOSITE, BOTTOM

Jones's 1884 design
depicted with the bascules
closed for the passage of
road traffic.

BELOW RIGHT

George Daniel Stevenson,
responsible for the
architecture of Tower
Bridge following the
death of Horace Jones.

Tower, London's greatest surviving medieval building, suggested that a medievalizing style was mandatory.

Jones's office employed a number of talented assistants well able to work in a Gothic manner. One of them was William Curtis Brangwyn (1837–1907), father of the artist Frank Brangwyn. He had run an architectural practice in the Belgian city of Bruges specializing in churches for a number of years before returning to England in the mid-1870s. (He later worked in south Wales with the ecclesiastical architect E. M. Bruce Vaughan, and died in Cardiff.) The extent of Brangwyn's input to the Tower Bridge designs is unclear. More significant was to be that of his sometime colleague, George Daniel Stevenson (1846–1931; see Chapter 3), but the key collaboration in the development of the project was with an engineer.

THE ARCHITECT AND THE ENGINEER

The relationship between architects and engineers has sometimes been as fraught as it has been creative. Bridge design was always an area where the two collided. One of Britain's most significant bridges is the Clifton Suspension Bridge (1864), spanning the Avon Gorge at Bristol and designed by Isambard Kingdom Brunel – an engineer. Waterloo Bridge (1811–17) was designed by the engineer John Rennie the elder (1761–1821) but completed after his death under the supervision of his

son John (1794–1874). It was widely admired and its demolition in the 1930s was deplored by many at a time when few thought highly of Tower Bridge. Waterloo Bridge was, however, a solid masonry structure of almost Roman grandeur that could be read as architecture.

When iron and then, increasingly, steel became the raw material for bridges, where was the role for the architect? Brunel was quite capable of designing Egyptian-style pylons (axed because of a lack of funding) for his Clifton bridge without the involvement of an architect. The ornamental touches added by the architect Matthew Digby Wyatt are incidental to the grandeur of Brunel's Paddington railway station. In the 1820s Thomas Telford had clothed his suspension bridge in Conwy, Wales, in a castellated Gothic manner in deference to the adjacent thirteenth-century castle.

Some critics found the cladding of Tower Bridge in Gothic masonry inappropriate and even immoral, but there were precedents for it. Unadorned engineering was seen in the Cannon Street and Blackfriars railway bridges. Both were completed in the mid-1860s – the latter replaced in the 1880s by a new bridge engineered by John Wolfe Barry – but they were generally condemned as blots on the river scene. Blackfriars Bridge was particularly lambasted by the art critic John Ruskin – never an enthusiast for railways – as showing 'an absence of all desire for beauty, of all joy in fancy, and of all freedom in thought'.[22]

The engineer John Wolfe Barry (1836–1918; he changed his surname to Wolfe-Barry in 1898) had been brought in by the City to assist Horace Jones. He did sterling work promoting the project before the Commons select committee. He was the youngest son of Sir Charles Barry (1795–1860), architect of the Palace of Westminster, and founded a hugely successful consultancy that flourished long into the twentieth century. He was also instrumental in the successful completion of London Underground's Circle Line in 1884. Barry worked on railway projects across Britain and in India and the Far East, and on new docks in Barry, Newport, Middlesbrough and Avonmouth. Knighted in 1897, he became president of the Institution of Civil Engineers and chairman of the Standards Institution. He had been effectively the founder of the latter organization, establishing the principle of standardization of components that made modern mass production possible.

Commenting on Jones's proposals in October 1884, Barry concluded that the best option was a bascule bridge: 'I think this bascule or lifting system of opening the centre span should not lightly be set aside, but should be thoroughly investigated.'[23] A low-level bascule bridge would remove the need for major roadworks at either end. Also, it 'would admit of a footway served by hydraulic lifts being practicable from shore to shore, when the bridge was open for river traffic'.[24] In a lecture delivered in 1893, when Tower Bridge was nearing completion, Barry recalled that he had 'become connected with the undertaking' in 1884.

Working with Jones, Barry was assisted by Henry Marc Brunel
(1842–1903; the second son of Isambard Kingdom Brunel), who
'supervised the whole of the complicated calculations and details of
the structure'.[25] Brunel had worked with Sir John Hawkshaw (1811–91)
between 1863 and 1866 on railway projects, including the utilitarian
Charing Cross railway bridge (which replaced his father's elegant
suspension bridge), and on an abortive Channel Tunnel scheme.
He entered into partnership with Barry in 1878.

Barry 'decided that any girders over the central span, when open
for ships, must be horizontal and not arched'.[26] A sketch of an
amended design – essentially that subsequently built – was shown
to the City's committee and formed the basis for the submission to
the Parliamentary committee in 1884. Addressing the latter, Barry
estimated that the bridge as proposed would take four years to build
and cost a total of £750,000, including construction work on the
approaches. Annual running costs would be £3,000–4,000. Barry
proposed to the City that he and Jones should share a fee commission
of 5%. However, the Bridge House Estates Committee felt, not
unreasonably, that Jones's work on the bridge was part of his duties
as City Architect and Surveyor, for which he was being well paid.
Eventually it was agreed that 'the sum of £30,000 should be paid to
Mr. Architect and Mr. Barry in such proportions as they may mutually
agree upon for their services in respect thereof'.[27] In the event, the

ABOVE LEFT
Henry Marc Brunel, the
business partner of John
Wolfe Barry from 1878.
He was a key figure in
the construction of
Tower Bridge.

ABOVE RIGHT
Invitation to the laying
of the foundation stone
('memorial stone')
of Tower Bridge.

OVERLEAF
The Prince of Wales, who
was deputed to carry out
the task by Queen Victoria,
laid the foundation stone
of Tower Bridge on 21 June
1886. Illustration from
The Graphic magazine
(26 June 1886).

bridge took eight years to build; another Act in 1889 authorized
extension of the construction period. The cost was over £1 million.

In March 1886 the City resolved to invite Queen Victoria to lay the
foundation stone for Tower Bridge. She deputed the task to the Prince
of Wales, later Edward VII. The ceremony took place on 21 June 1886,
work on the foundations having begun in April. It was a grand occasion,
with the Corporation's members and officers out in force and MPs
and peers in attendance. 'Upwards of 200 visitors from India and the
colonies, who had come over for the Colonial and India Exhibition
[in South Kensington], were invited to be present.'[20] A large marquee
accommodated more than 1,500 guests. The band of the Coldstream
Guards played and a choir sang. The Bishop of London pronounced
a blessing. A speech by the City Recorder (a senior legal officer)
expressed the self-congratulatory mood of the Corporation, whose
'careful husbanding and management' of the Bridge House Estates had
made the project possible. The event could have ended in tragedy, since
Horace Jones had narrowly escaped death 'by the falling of part of one
of the machines in use'. Within months he received a knighthood but
he never saw the completed bridge, as he died in May 1887. But with
Barry as coordinator, an outstanding team saw the project to fruition.

3 | BUILDING TOWER BRIDGE

FORM AND MATERIALS

THE FINAL FORM OF TOWER BRIDGE had been agreed in 1885: a central lifting span, with the lifting machinery housed in two great towers, and two subsidiary approach spans anchored in abutments on the shore. The two towers, which were to make Tower Bridge an iconic structure, recalled the fortified bridges of the Middle Ages. Perhaps the most obvious precedent was the fourteenth-century Valentré bridge in the French city of Cahors. But there were more recent ones, notably in Germany, where a number of railway bridges assumed a fortified appearance. The most elaborate example was the Cathedral Bridge over the Rhine in Cologne, completed in 1859 to designs by the engineer Hermann Lohse. It had great castellated gatehouses, fitted with gates to open and close the line, at either end, by the architect Heinrich Strack. The elaborate form of this bridge doubtless owed much to its location, close to Cologne Cathedral, the most famous medieval monument in Germany.

OPPOSITE, TOP
The Cathedral Bridge in Cologne, completed in 1859, was an iron structure with castellated towers at either end, providing a possible model for Tower Bridge. Cologne Cathedral, like the Tower of London, was a national monument and the design of the bridge deferred to it.

OPPOSITE, BOTTOM
Watercolour by John Crowther of the Tower of London from Pickle Herring Wharf at low tide, c. 1883. By this date antiquarian restoration of the Tower had been proceeding for thirty years, accentuating the building's status as a Romantic monument and a tourist attraction.

Tower Bridge as built benefited from the input of John Wolfe Barry. The great arch initially proposed by Horace Jones for the central span had been abandoned and upper-level footways introduced. This allowed ample clearance for the tallest ship masts. Detailed design work began during 1885 ready for a start on site the following year. Jones and Barry, architect and engineer, worked in an apparently harmonious partnership, 'apportioning the duties between them, but each to be responsible to the Corporation for the whole'.[1] The issue of appointing contractors for the bridge's construction was soon a priority. The core material was to be steel, which, from the 1880s on, began to replace cast and wrought iron as a building component. Paris's Eiffel Tower, completed in 1889, was a late example of large-scale iron construction. Significantly, the mighty Forth Bridge, opened a year later, was a steel structure; the first rail bridge over the river Tay, which had collapsed disastrously in 1879, had been constructed of iron. Steel had the advantage of being lighter, stronger and more fire-resistant than iron.

Tower Bridge was to be clad in non-structural masonry, largely as a gesture towards the Tower of London next to it. W. Harrison Ainsworth's novel *The Tower of London: A Romance* (1840) established the credentials of the Tower as a Romantic monument. The medievalizing restoration and partial rebuilding, begun by the architect Anthony Salvin (1799–1881) in the 1850s (and continued into the first decades of the twentieth century under other hands), further increased its picturesque appeal. 'When the opening bridge was first proposed', Barry wrote, 'there was some outcry by aesthetical people lest it should ruin the picturesqueness of the Tower of London by hideous girder erections, and it seemed to be the universal wish that this bridge should be in harmony architecturally with the Tower.'[2]

The approval of the Tower authorities and the War Office was necessary for the construction of the northern approach road, which impinged on the Tower ditch. The Tower was still under royal jurisdiction and garrisoned. There were 'long negotiations' with the City of London, Barry recorded. Reassured that the look of the bridge would be in keeping with its setting, they demanded that 'new works should be made suitable for the mounting of guns and for military occupation'.[3] In practice, this meant setting aside one of the arches beneath the road for use as a guardroom. In fact guns were mounted on the bridge during the First World War in response to Zeppelin raids by German forces. The Yeoman Warders of the Tower, to their annoyance, lost an area that they used as allotments. The construction of the southern approach road had not even been begun when the bridge opened. 'The London County Council are wholly in arrear with their share of the undertaking', Barry complained.[4]

CONSTRUCTING THE FOUNDATIONS

The whole construction process, begun in 1886, was overseen on site by Barry's resident engineer (and later a partner in his practice), George Cruttwell (1857–1933), 'a patient, watchful man'.[5] He donned waders and oilskin clothing to superintend every phase of the work, much of it in the river and its muddy foreshore. Before work could begin on the superstructure, the foundations for the bridge had to be constructed. It was to be, as Barry later recalled, 'troublesome and tedious, owing to the isolation of the piers, and still more to the great amount of river traffic, rendering the berthing of barges difficult'.[6] The shore abutments could be constructed using conventional cofferdams. In essence these were timber enclosures, sunk into the mud and then pumped out to create a dry working space. The two great towers would house the machinery for lifting the central span and carry the chains bearing the northern and southern approach spans, as well as the upper pedestrian walkway. As a result they had to sit on massive piers in the bed of the Thames. They were sunk into the hard London clay to a depth of 25 ft (7.6 m), an extraordinarily demanding undertaking.

The piers were constructed using caissons since, as Cruttwell recalled, 'Parliament forbade the sinking of a cofferdam into the bed of the Thames.'[7] Caissons had been developed in the eighteenth century. They were used in the construction of Westminster Bridge, completed in 1750, by the Swiss engineer Charles Labelye (1705–81). More recently they had been employed for the great piers sunk in New York's East River to support the Brooklyn Bridge, completed in 1883. The caissons were basically large moveable cylinders of wrought iron, a quarter to half an inch

BELOW

Plan and elevation of Tower Bridge as built, with details of various elements of its structure, as reproduced in the *Minutes of Proceedings of The Institution of Civil Engineers* (1896–97).

OVERLEAF

Drawing of caissons and staging used to construct the foundations of Tower Bridge, as illustrated in *The Engineer*, vol. 76 (15 December 1893).

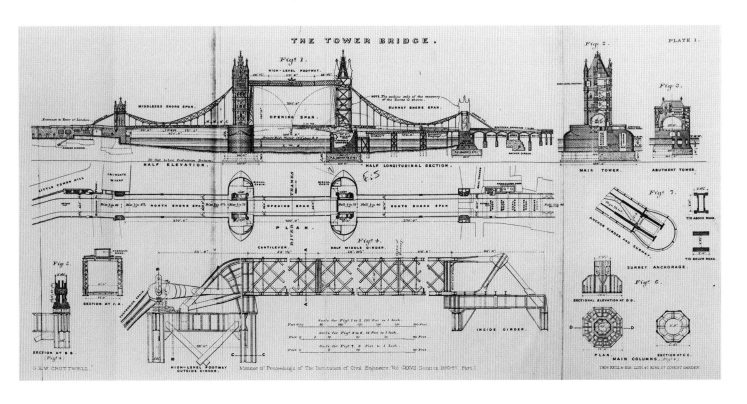

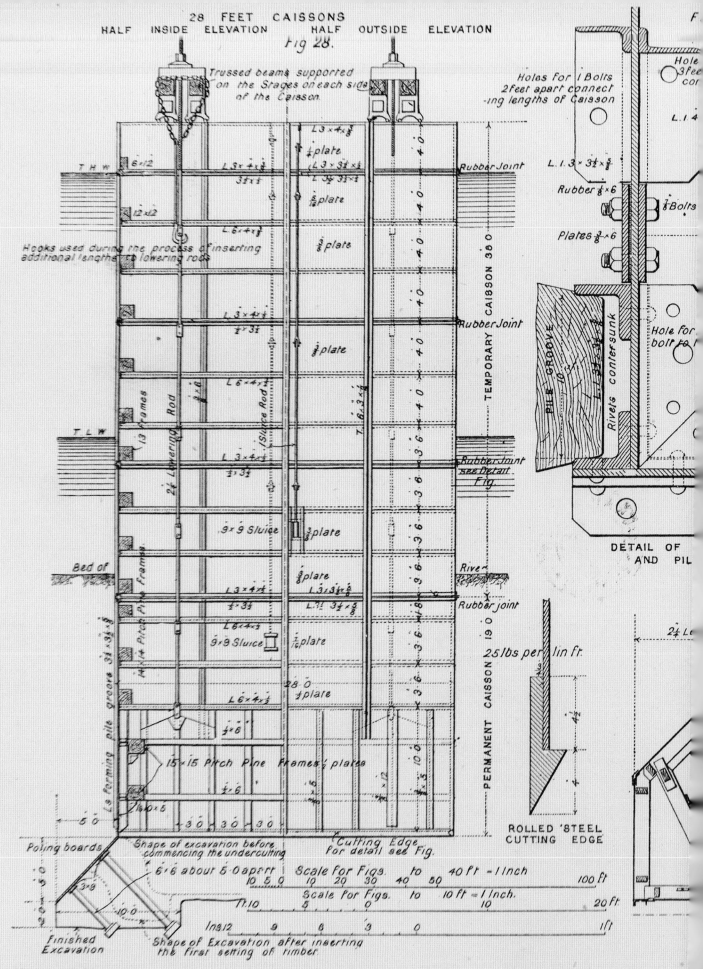

Trussed beams supported on the Stages on each side of the Caisson.

Holes for 1 Bolts 2 feet apart connect -ing lengths of Caisson

Hole 3 feet cor

T.H.W.   6 × 12   L 3 × 4 × ⅜
½ plate
L 3 × 3½ × ½   L.I.4

3 × ½   L 3½ × 3½ × ½
⅜ plate   Rubber Joint

12 × 2   L 6 × 4 × ½
⅜ plate   L.I. 3 × 3½ × ½

Rubber ¼ × 6   ¼ Bolts

Hooks used during the process of inserting additional lengths to lowering rod   Plates ⅜ × 6

L 3 × 4 × ½
¼ × 3½   Rubber Joint
⅜ plate

T.L.W.   L 6 × 4 × ½   PILE GROOVE

L 3 × 4 × ½   Hole for
¼ × 3½   Rubber Joint bolt to
9 × 9 Sluice   ⅜ plate   see Detail Fig.

DETAIL OF
AND PIL

Rivets contersunk

Bed of   ½ plate
L 3 × 4 × ½   L 3 × 3½ × ½
¼ × 3½   River
L 6 × 4 × ½   L.I. 3½ × ⅝   Rubber joint
9 × 9 Sluice   ⅞ plate   25 lbs per lin ft.

L 6 × 4 × ½   28 0
½ plate

ROLLED STEEL
CUTTING EDGE

15 × 15 Pitch Pine Frames, plates
¼ × 6

10 × 6

Poling boards   Shape of excavation before commencing the undercutting   Cutting Edge for detail see Fig.

Finished Excavation   Shape of Excavation after inserting the first setting of timber

6 × 6 about 5 0 apart   Scale for Figs.   to   40 ft = 1 inch
10 5 0   10   20   30   40   50   100 ft

Scale for Figs.   to   10 ft = 1 inch.
ft 10   5   0   10   20 ft.

1 in 12   9   6   3   0   1 ft

TEMPORARY CAISSON 38 0   PERMANENT CAISSON 19 0

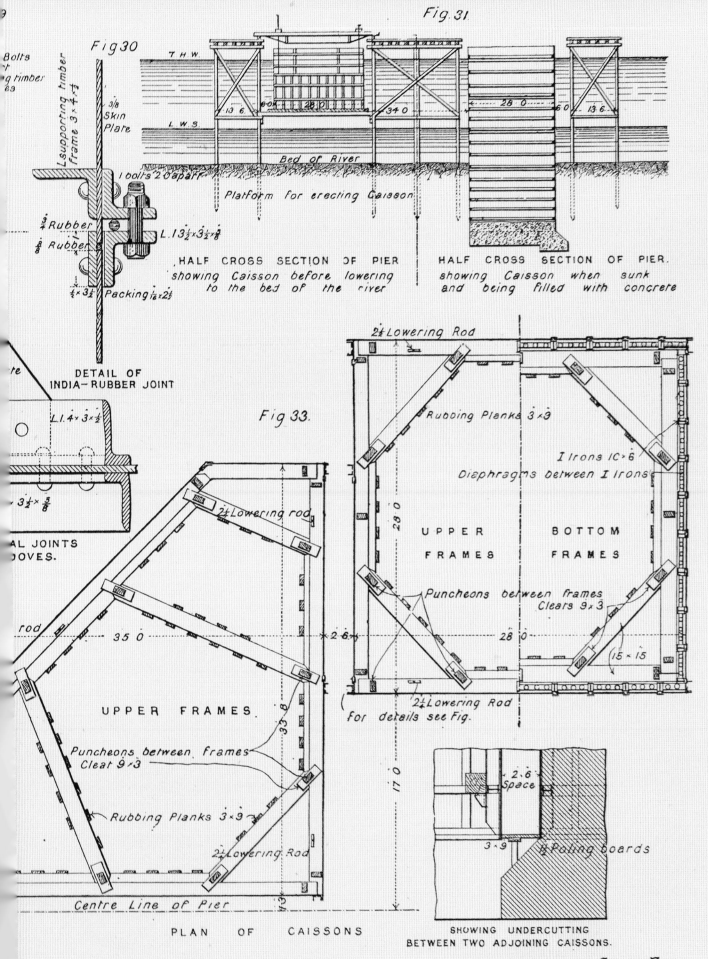

Fig 30

Fig. 31

Bolts

g timber
23

L supporting timber
frame 3 × 4 × 4

3/8 Skin Plate

T.H.W.

L.W.S.

13 6   60 0   28 0   34 0   28 0   60 0   13 6

Bed of River

bolts 2 0 apart

Platform for erecting Caisson

3/4 Rubber

3/8 Rubber

L. 13½ × 3½ × ⅜

½ × 3½   Packing ⅛ × 2½

DETAIL OF
INDIA-RUBBER JOINT

HALF CROSS SECTION OF PIER
showing Caisson before lowering
to the bed of the river

HALF CROSS SECTION OF PIER.
showing Caisson when sunk
and being filled with concrete

L.I. 4 × 3 × ½

× 3½ × ⅜

AL JOINTS
OVES.

2¼ Lowering Rod

Fig 33.

Rubbing Planks 3 × 9

I Irons 10 × 6
Diaphragms between I Irons

UPPER
FRAMES

BOTTOM
FRAMES

28 0

2¼ Lowering rod

Puncheons between frames
Clears 9 × 3

35 0

2 6

28 0

15 × 15

rod

33 8

UPPER   FRAMES.

Puncheons between frames
Cleat 9 × 3

2¼ Lowering Rod
for details see Fig.

Rubbing Planks 3 × 9

17 0

2.6
Space

2¼ Lowering Rod

3 · 9   8 Poling boards

Centre Line of Pier

PLAN   OF   CAISSONS

SHOWING UNDERCUTTING
BETWEEN TWO ADJOINING CAISSONS.

SWAIN ENG.

BUILDING FOUNDATIONS

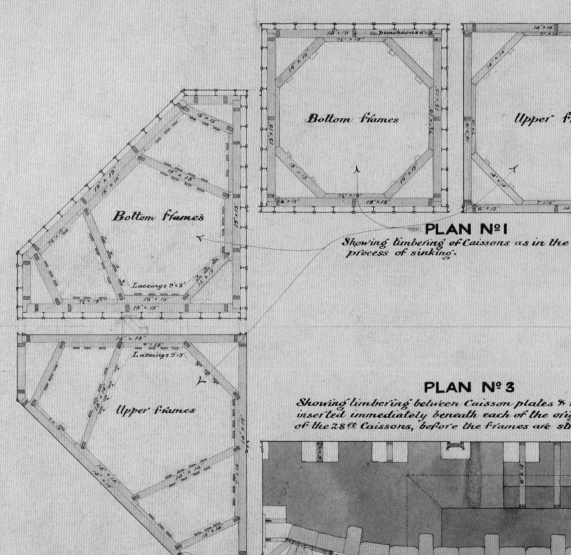

Bottom frames

Upper frames

puncheons 6"

Bottom frames

Lacings 3"×3"

Lacings 3"×3"

Upper frames

PLAN Nº1
Showing timbering of Caissons as in the process of sinking.

PLAN Nº 3
Showing timbering between Caisson plates & masonry inserted immediately beneath each of the original fram of the 28ᶠᵗ Caissons, before the frames are struck.

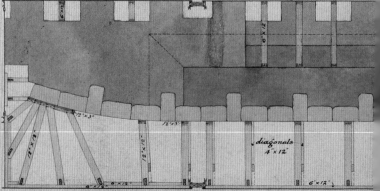

diagonals 4"×12"

le Caissons.

inch

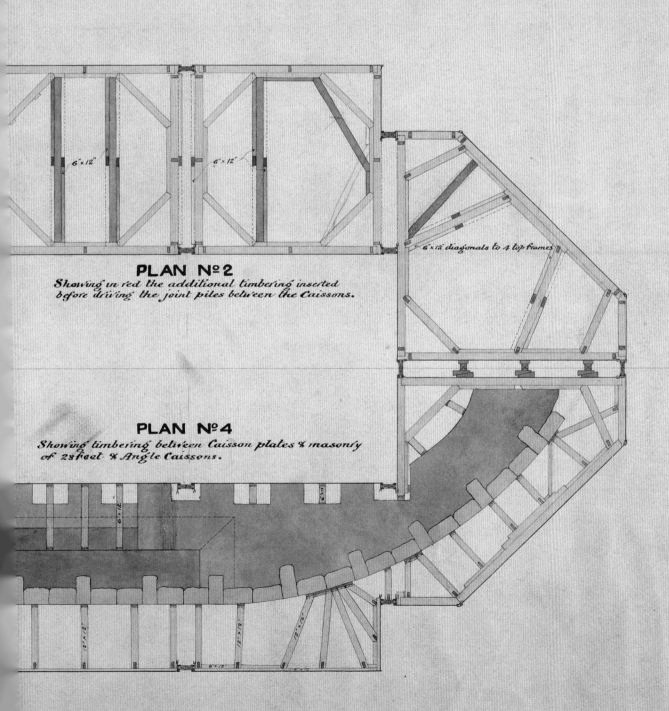

6"× 12"   6"× 12"

6"× 12" diagonals to 4 top frames

PLAN Nº 2
Showing in red the additional timbering inserted
before driving the joint piles between the Caissons.

PLAN Nº 4
Showing timbering between Caisson plates & masonry
of 28 feet & Angle Caissons.

PREVIOUS

Colour drawing showing
timber staging used in
constructing caissons.

OPPOSITE, TOP

Work proceeding on the
masonry of the tower piers
of the bridge.

OPPOSITE, BOTTOM

View from the river of
the tower piers under
construction.

BELOW LEFT

Tower on the Brooklyn side
of Brooklyn Bridge under
construction, c. 1878. The
bridge was opened in 1883.

BELOW RIGHT

A 1906 photograph of
William Walker, the diver
who worked on repairing
the flooded foundations
of Winchester Cathedral
between 1906 and 1912.
At Tower Bridge divers dug
out clay and gravel to sink
caissons into the riverbed.

(0.6 to 1.2 cm) thick. They were fabricated by Messrs Head, Wrightson & Co. and delivered to the site in four pieces, each 19 ft (5.7 m) high.

At Tower Bridge there were twelve caissons to each pier, lowered, using a system of screws and rods, into the river. Triangular caissons were fabricated for the cutwater projections at the base of each tower. On top of the permanent caissons further lengths of iron were erected temporarily to reach above high-water level, the whole assembly extending some 60 ft (18 m). The iron sheets were joined together with rubber seals. Divers were sent down to dig out layers of clay and gravel, which were craned up into barges. The permanent caissons sank down, penetrating some 5–10 ft (1.5–3 m) into the clay. When the spaces within them had been pumped out and made watertight, workers were able to descend and dig out the remainder of the clay.

The process was anything but trouble-free. 'Blows' occurred, with the river water rushing in, necessitating pumping. As Barry commented, 'it is comparatively easy to prevent a caisson from going wrong (as is the case with many animate subjects as well as inanimate) by timely control, but it is a very different thing to put the matter right when a wrong course has been pronouncedly taken'.[8] Working in the river was, in any case, bound to be difficult, laborious and even dangerous. On one occasion, a number of workers were stranded overnight on one of the piers when a dense London fog descended and boats were unable to set out to rescue them.

Following the completion of the excavation work, the permanent caissons were filled with concrete to support the brickwork and masonry above. The first pier had to be largely complete before work could begin on the second. This was because there were strict restrictions on any obstruction to the passage of shipping – a minimum width of 160 ft (48 m) had to be kept clear – and the staging needed for the construction work extended some distance into the river. As Barry pointed out, barges delivering materials were not permitted to moor within the central waterway. The contract for all this work, together with the abutments at either side of the river (costed at £131,344), was let to John Jackson (1851–1919) of Victoria Chambers, Westminster.

Jackson represented a new breed of contractor: a qualified engineer as well as a businessman and willing to get his hands dirty. Family connections took him into the construction business – an uncle was George Myers, the favoured builder of the famed Gothic Revival architect A. W. N. Pugin. (Myers had been the contractor for one of Horace Jones's earliest works, a church at Cherry Burton in Yorkshire, completed in 1852. With Jones as City Architect, he was also responsible for the iron roof over the council chamber at the Guildhall.) With his brother William, John Jackson worked in Newcastle upon Tyne for William Armstrong on buildings at the Elswick works and on Armstrong's country house, Cragside, near Rothbury, as well as on the Swing Bridge. He then studied engineering

7

8

9

10

11

12

SCALE 8 FEET TO AN INCH

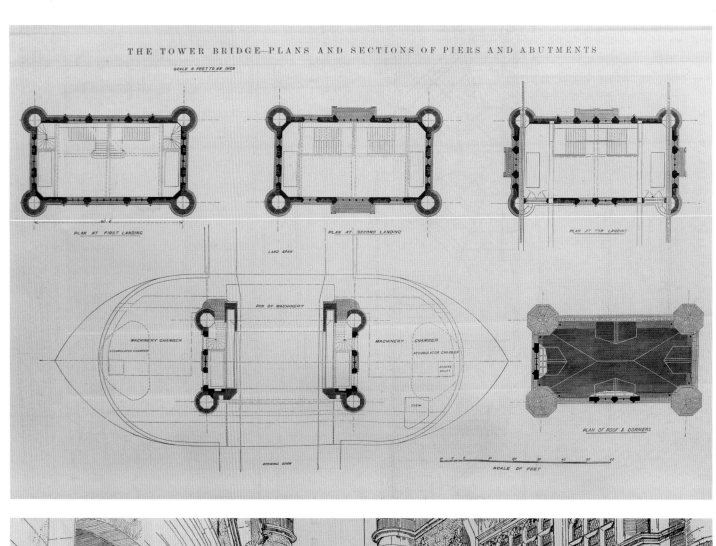

PLAN AT FIRST LANDING

PLAN AT SECOND LANDING

PLAN AT TOP LANDING

LAND SPAN

PIN OF MACHINERY

MACHINERY CHAMBER

MACHINERY CHAMBER

ACCUMULATOR CHAMBER

ACCUMULATOR CHAMBER

ACCESS SHAFT

CABIN

OPENING SPAN

PLAN OF ROOF & DORMERS

SCALE OF FEET

Plans and sections of the
piers and abutments of
the bridge, reproduced
in *The Engineer*, vol. 76
(15 December 1893).

OPPOSITE, BOTTOM

The masonry arches over
the northern abutment
of the bridge, illustrated
in *The Engineer*, vol. 76
(15 December 1893).

BELOW

The bridge nearing
completion. The work on
the substructure had taken
four years to finish, much
longer than envisaged.

at Edinburgh University. His burgeoning business took him to
Glasgow and then in 1880 to London. He was knighted in 1895 and
entered Parliament in 1910, having completed dock and railway projects
across four continents. These included a line across the Andes in South
America and the new Barry Docks in south Wales in conjunction with
John Wolfe Barry.

The Bridge House Estates Committee, visiting the Tower Bridge
site in 1888, was clearly pleased with the progress of work. It 'hoped
that the contractor might live long to enjoy the rewards of having his
name associated with so important and unique an undertaking'.[9] A year
later, in contrast, the Committee was complaining loudly about delays.
The work on the substructure took four years to complete, considerably
longer than had been anticipated and a reflection of the complexity
of the process. The restrictions imposed by the Thames Conservancy,
relating to any obstruction of the passage along the river, were blamed.

BUILDING THE SUPERSTRUCTURE

In contrast Barry was to write after the completion of the project, 'the erection of the superstructure of the bridge has been effected without any considerable difficulty'.[10] As late as the middle of 1889 work had not begun on the superstructure but soon after it was proceeding rapidly. This was due in large part to the process of steelwork prefabrication devised by Barry with the steel fabricators William Arrol & Co. of Dalmarnock, Glasgow. William Arrol (1839–1913) was born in Renfrewshire and had trained as a blacksmith from the age of thirteen. He used his modest savings to start out in business in 1868 and established the Dalmarnock works in 1872. His operations expanded rapidly. In 1882 he won the contract for the new railway bridge over the river Tay, replacing that which had disastrously collapsed in 1879. He went on to build the Forth Bridge and, on its completion, was knighted. He entered Parliament as a Liberal MP in 1895.

Arrol won the Tower Bridge contract in July 1889. It provided for the supply and erection on site of 11,000 tons of steelwork, together with 1,200 tons of ornamental cast iron. Coordination between steel manufacturer and engineer was ensured by Barry's posting an assistant, C. J. Jackaman, on site at Dalmarnock. Jackaman tested the quality of the steel as it was produced, ready for dispatch to the site. 'The girder, or other piece of constructional work, when riveted up so far as can be

BELOW
Portrait of Sir William Arrol. The steelwork for Tower Bridge was fabricated in his Clydeside works.

OPPOSITE, TOP
The Forth Bridge, in a photograph of c. 1890. Winning the contract to fabricate the steelwork for this bridge was a landmark in Arrol's career. He was knighted on its completion.

OPPOSITE, BOTTOM
Arrol's Dalmarnock works, c. 1900, showing the portable riveting machine devised by Arrol in operation. This piece of equipment was used in the construction of the steelwork on Tower Bridge.

done at the works, is painted or oiled, and marked for erection purposes.'[11] Arrol & Co., in turn, appointed J. E. Tuit as its representative in London. However, William Arrol took a close personal interest in the project and was a familiar figure on the Glasgow-to-London expresses when travelling to the bridge site.

Tower Bridge was, in many respects, a Scottish product. Additional steelwork was supplied by The Steel Company of Scotland and several other Glasgow-based manufacturers. Ornamental cast-iron parapets and decorative panels applied to the upper walkways were made by Fullerton, Hodgart & Barclay of Paisley. Up to 100 tons of steel per week were brought from Scotland by sea, with the ships of the Clyde Shipping and Carron companies unloading their cargo into barges serving the site. Any element required urgently was dispatched by rail.

Soon after winning the contract, Arrol began the fabrication of the steel columns of the river piers. These frame each tower, and support the high-level walkways and the chains for the side spans. Temporary staging made of timber on steel beams was built from the shore on both sides of the river to the piers. Rails to carry cranes were laid on top. Timber staging at the base of the towers was kept in place to support further work. The structure of the main towers consisted of four great octagonal steel columns connected by three layers of girders, reinforced by wind bracing. The columns were craned into position in sections and then riveted together by teams of men working from moveable timber platforms and progressing steadily upwards. A good squad, J. E. Tuit recalled in his memoir of the project, 'was able to put in about two hundred ⁷/₈ inch [2.2 cm] rivets in a day of ten hours'.[12] On areas of the structure that were easier to access, a hydraulic riveting machine devised by Arrol was used. In total, more than 13 million rivets were used in the construction of the bridge.

One function of the main towers was to carry the upper walkways, which would be served by lifts as well as staircases. These were built as cantilevered girders from each side using cranes on the top landings. The linking section was inserted by cranes positioned on top of the cantilevers. The walkways were then assembled, with cast-iron panelling, mouldings and tracery, and zinc-clad timber roofs. Timber staging was placed below the walkways to ensure that falling pieces of metal or tools did not land on vessels passing below. 'This last consideration was one of the greatest importance, since many pleasure steamers, crowded with passengers, continually passing under these footways, necessitated the greatest care on the part of the contractors.'[13] There were no reported accidents.

The central opening span of the bridge, 200 ft (60 m) across, consisted of two leaves. Each turned on a steel pivot weighing 25 tons, and carried a roadway 32 ft (10 m) wide, flanked by pedestrian footways. The leaves pivot into great chambers, which are majestic, awesome spaces. Each leaf was carried on four girders. A counterbalance box attached to each of the landward ends of the girders was filled with 422 tons of lead (expensive but economical of space) and iron ballast. The main pivoting element of each leaf weighed 621 tons, so when the leaf opened its total mass was over 1,000 tons.

OPPOSITE

A photograph taken in June 1892 of the north tower from the south tower. It shows the bascule girders being installed and the masonry cladding having reached first-floor level.

BELOW

Early in 1894, with the opening of the bridge imminent, the stability of the structure was tested. As reported in the publication *St James's Budget* in June that year, the roadway was loaded with 'five heavy steamrollers and a number of trucks, each laden with metal and heavy refuse'.

The Tower Bridge Act specified that there should be 160 ft (49 m) of clear water at all times so that barges and ships could access the Pool of London. Therefore the girders had to be erected vertically, and the roadway, together with its flooring of timber blocks on a base of corrugated steel floor plates, applied in this position. Nothing in the construction of the bridge was anything less than challenging. Yet the team of engineers and contractors addressed each potential problem with typically Victorian energy and ingenuity. In the spring of 1894, with the bridge's opening imminent, the stability of the central opening section was tested by loading it with a weight of 150 tons, provided by steamrollers and carts of ballast. The 270-ft (82-m) long side spans of the bridge, connecting the approach roads to the towers, are suspension bridges. One of George Daniel Stevenson's significant contributions to the final design was to add at each end on the landward side impressive and highly picturesque gatehouses, reminiscent perhaps of those that had guarded the old London Bridge. In contrast, Jones had proposed little more than enormous gateposts to carry the chains. The chains were massive, resembling girders and weighing around 1 ton for every foot of their length. As Barry explained,

the object of the form is to distribute the local loads due to passing traffic, which in the case of an ordinary suspension bridge, depress

each part of the chain as the load passes, and consequently distort the platform of the bridge. By making the chain, as it were, double, and bracing it with iron triangulations, these local deflections are avoided.[14]

In other words, the form of the chains, which do resemble girders, was intended to avoid any impact on the roadway of very heavy loads.

Constructing the chains was a difficult operation, with very substantial timber staging put in place to support the cranes used. A travelling gantry was built to carry a steam-powered crane, with a jib 70 ft (21 m) long. It was used to assemble those parts out of reach of the cranes positioned on the landward side of the spans, where the chains were anchored. The two sections of chain were pinned together so that there was a firm structural connection right across the river. The road sections of the side spans were filled with concrete on top of the steel floor plates, and topped by wood paving blocks. Cast-iron parapets were fitted along each side of the bridge, some of them emblazoned with the arms of the City. All exposed steelwork was given three coats of paint, the last being 'bright chocolate'. This colour scheme survived until battleship grey was applied as camouflage in the 1940s.

GEORGE DANIEL STEVENSON AND THE DESIGN OF TOWER BRIDGE

Horace Jones had left the architecture of Tower Bridge only vaguely sketched out at the time of his death in 1887. However, by then he had substituted a mix of brick and stone cladding for the brick he had initially proposed. The detailed designs were made by one of his assistants, George Daniel (G. D.) Stevenson (1846–1931), who had begun to work on them in 1884 and later established his own practice on the basis of the commission. Stevenson had worked in the office of George Somers Clarke (1822–82), a pupil of Charles Barry. Clarke's works include a number of churches as well as many domestic projects. The most important of the latter was Wyfold Court, a lavish country house in Oxfordshire built in 1872–76 for a Lancashire cotton magnate.

By the late 1870s Stevenson was an assistant to Horace Jones. After leaving the City's employ, he set up his own office in King Street, off Cheapside. An anonymous correspondent, 'Honour to whom honour is due', wrote to *Building News* in 1894: 'it is an open secret that Mr. G. D. Stevenson prepared the drawings for Sir Horace Jones, and on the death of the latter he was engaged by the Corporation to prepare the details, but not one daily paper, so far as I know, mentioned his name.'

An extraordinary cache of drawings of Tower Bridge, now in the London Metropolitan Archives, confirms the extent of Stevenson's

BELOW LEFT
Elevation of one of the towers facing the bridge opening section.

OPPOSITE
These drawings (on pp. 96–101) by G. D. Stevenson of elevations, sections and details of the bridge, all dated 1889, were discovered in his former home only in 1974. This elevation is of the landward-facing side of one of the towers. The section reveals the nature of the tower's construction: a thin layer of masonry on a steel frame.

OVERLEAF, LEFT
Detailed elevational treatment of one of the towers.

OVERLEAF, RIGHT
Detail of the angle pinnacles and dormers at the top of one of the towers.

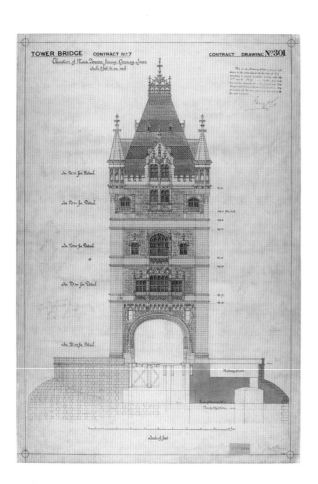

TOWER BRIDGE

CONTRACT Nº 7

Elevation of Main Tower facing Land Span & Longitudinal Section
Scale 8 feet to an inch.

CONTRACT DRAWING Nº 302

See Nº 303 for Detail of Roof

Elevation.

Section on line A.B.

Scale of feet.

Trinity High Water 112.50

Limit of Contract Nº 1 116.50

21/12/447

TOWER BRIDGE

CONTRACT N°7

CONTRACT   DRAWING N°307

Fine Axed Granite.   Rock Faced Granite.

Note
See N° 306
for Detail of
Niche
which occurs
on Land span
sides only.

Note
All intersecting
joints of Mullions
and Transoms to
have Slate Dowels
1 in. square 2½ long.

Quadrant.

Elevation.

Notes
See N°s 300, 301, 302 for General Elevations.
Light Grey tint on Elevation denotes fine
Axed granite.
Dark Grey, Rock Faced Granite.
Brown tint, Portland Stone.
The whole of which are to be fixed with all
proper & necessary Slate Dovetail Cramps,
Slate and copper Dowels, Cement joggles
&c to be well
bonded grouted
and pointed to
Brick backings.

Section.

Slate Dovetail Cramps
8 x 4 x 2" thick sunk 1"in top
and bottom beds.

Plan of 1st Stage.

Plan through AB.

Scale of feet.

Plan of Second Stage Windows.

21/12/452

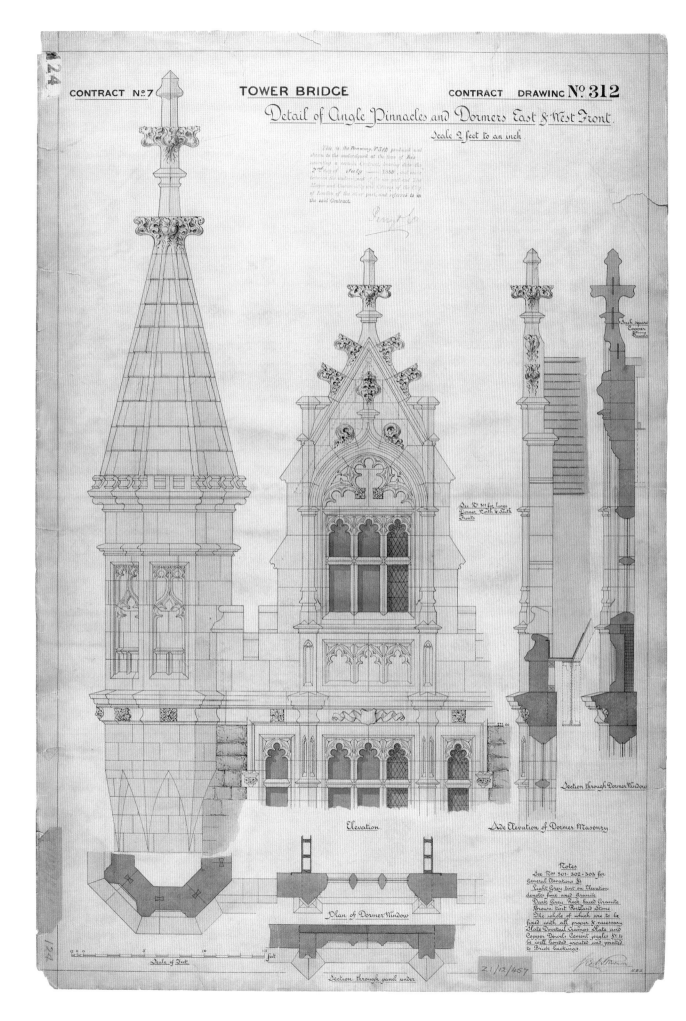

CONTRACT Nº 7   TOWER BRIDGE   CONTRACT DRAWING Nº 312

Detail of Angle Pinnacles and Dormers East & West Front.

Scale 2 feet to an inch

This is the Drawing Nº 312 produced and
shewn to the undersigned at the time of his
executing a certain Contract, bearing date the
2ⁿᵈ day of July ——— 1886, and made
between the undersigned of the one part and The
Mayor and Commonalty and Citizens of the City
of London of the other part, and referred to in
the said Contract.

See Nº 311 for large
Dormer North & South
Fronts

Inch square
Copper Dowels

Elevation.

Side Elevation of Dormer Masonry.

Section through Dormer Window

Plan of Dormer Window

Section through panel under

Scale of Feet.

5   10   15   feet

Z. 1/12/457

Notes
See Nos 301·302·303 for
General Elevations &
Light Grey Tint on Elevation
denotes fine axed Granite
Dark Grey Rock faced Granite
Brown Tint Portland Stone
The whole of which are to be
fixed with all proper & necessary
Slate Dovetail cramps Slate and
Copper Dowels Cement joggles &c to
be well bonded grouted and pointed
to Brick backings

TOWER BRIDGE
CONTRACT N°. 7

Middlesex Abutment Tower.
Scale 8 feet to an inch.

183. 37

140. 00

Limit of Contract N°. 2

Trinity High Water 112. 50

Half Elevation River Side.

Half Elevation Land Side.

Longitudinal Section

Plan.

Half Plan Roof.

20   5   0

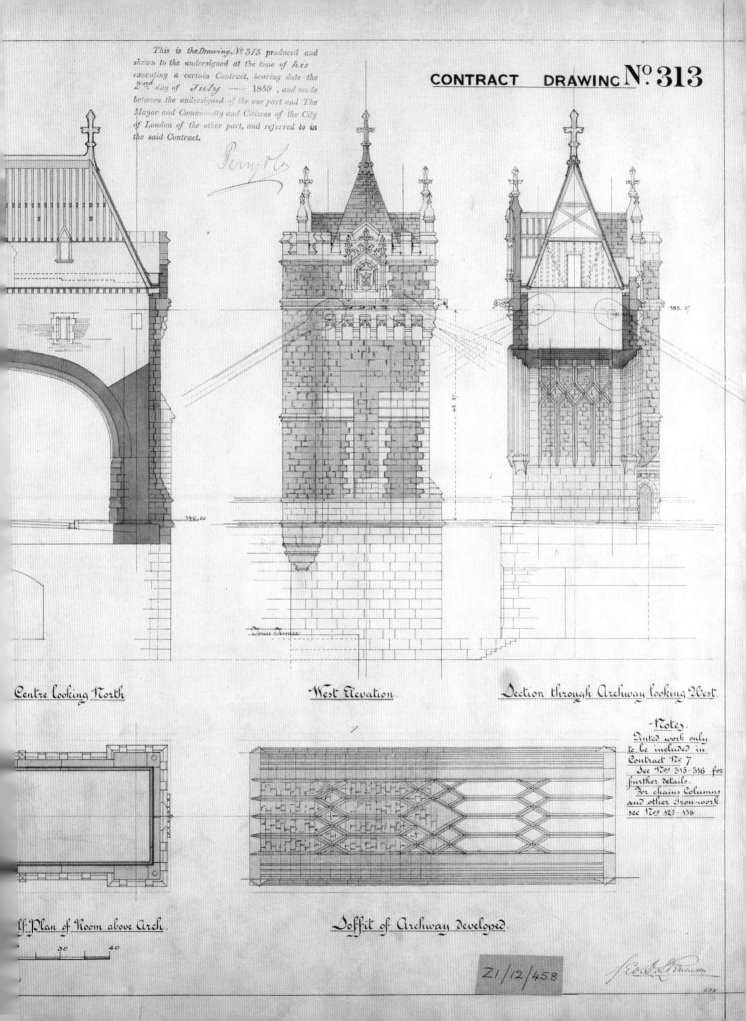

CONTRACT DRAWING No. 313

Centre looking North.

West Elevation.

Section through Archway looking West.

Plan of Room above Arch.

Soffit of Archway developed.

Z1/12/458

contribution to the project. These were discovered in 1974 in the cellar of the house in Wood Green, north London, where Stevenson had lived in retirement. They are superbly executed, in pen and colour wash. Stevenson's architecture, it is sometimes suggested, has a rather Scottish flavour. Yet the granite that is the principal ingredient of the architectural clothing of the bridge came not from Aberdeenshire but from Cornwall. The same material had been used in the construction of the Eddystone Lighthouse off the southern coast. Windows, parapets and pinnacles were executed using Portland stone, used in major public buildings such as St Paul's Cathedral. Underneath the stone cladding is a layer of brick. Stevenson was responsible for every decorative element of the bridge, including the ornamental parapets and panels for the high-level walkways. He also designed the lamp standards. The 'high-power flat-flame gas lamps' were made by William Sugg & Co. of Westminster.[15] The company was also responsible for manufacturing the gas and water mains, hydrants, water tanks, and gates and railings.

The masonry cladding was not purely decorative; as Barry explained,

it was clear that in any event a large part of the steelwork of the towers must be enclosed in some material, for the moving quadrants project upwards some forty feet [12 m] from the level of the roadway, while the stairs and lifts also required protection from the weather. It thus became a question of surrounding the towers either with cast

PREVIOUS
Various plans, sections and elevations of the bridge drawn by G. D. Stevenson, dated 1889.

BELOW LEFT
An advertisement in Building News in June 1894 for Sugg's gas lamps. The company won the contract for the lighting on the bridge, where gas lighting continued in use well into the 20th century.

OPPOSITE
A view of the north tower, dated September 1892, shows bascule girders under construction and granite masonry cladding being applied. The chains of the north shore span have been completed.

OVERLEAF
With the steel structure of the bridge virtually complete, masonry rises up the north tower. The stone cladding was functional as well as decorative, protecting the steelwork from the weather.

WER BRIDGE WORKS SEP 24th 1892

iron panelling or with stone, and eventually a granite facing, with Portland stone dressings, was adopted.[16]

There were clear advantages in the use of stone over iron, as the latter was subject to corrosion. Barry conceded that 'some purists will say that the lamp of truth has been sadly neglected in this combination of materials, and that the architects of classical or medieval times would not have sanctioned such an arrangement as a complex structure of steel surrounded by stone'.[17] ('Purists' did, indeed, express criticisms of the bridge along those lines.) But the architects of those past eras did not have the option of using iron and steel. Sir Christopher Wren, it might be said, had been culpable of a sham when he used a hidden brick cone to support the dome of St Paul's Cathedral in the seventeenth century. In any case, Barry concluded, 'if the appearance of Tower Bridge is approved, we may forget that the towers have skeletons as much concealed as that of the human body, of which we do not think when we contemplate examples of manly or feminine beauty'.[18]

The contract for the masonry superstructure was let to Perry & Co. This well-established company had grown steadily – eventually employing 5,000 men – under the direction of Herbert Henry Bartlett (1842–1921), who joined the firm in 1872. The stone, cut and dressed by machine, was brought in by barge. Some 235,000 cubic feet (6,654 cubic metres) of granite were used, along with 31 million bricks. Men worked on

timber stages suspended on wires – there was little scaffolding. This method was, by present-day standards, hazardous, but only 6 men out of up to 800 employed died as a result of accidents on site, 'and at least one of these was the result of a sudden illness, or of a fit'.[19] Steam-powered cranes lifted the stone. Each layer was carried on the girders positioned at each stage of the towers so that the masonry skin was lighter in weight than it would have been if raised continuously up from the road level. This approach also resulted in economies in the quantity of stone required. The masonry skin was seen very much as a non-structural element. Tuit recorded that:

> in order to prevent any adhesion between the masonry and the steelwork at the Tower Bridge, the columns were covered with canvas as the masonry was built around them, and spaces were left in such places where any subsequent compression of the steelwork would bring undue weight upon the adjacent stonework.[20]

The construction of the bridge was well recorded, not only in photographs but also in the drawings of work in progress commissioned by *The Graphic* magazine from the French artist Henri Lanos (1859–1929). These works represent well the sheer drama of the undertaking. Men are depicted walking along girders high above the river, with none of the safety devices mandatory today.

THE OPENING OF TOWER BRIDGE

The bridge was formally opened on 30 June 1894. The Prince and Princess of Wales returned to again represent Queen Victoria at what was, *The Times* reported, 'a picturesque and stately ceremonial, perfectly performed under the most favourable conditions…. The glorious sunshine brought out in full relief the many beauties of the great display and of the noble river which all true Englishmen love with a proud affection as the chiefest glory of their ancient capital.' A large silver urn had been set up on the platform where the Prince and Princess and assorted VIPs were seated. By turning a small handle on top of the urn the Prince symbolically set the bascules in motion – the spectators 'gave vent to their admiration and delight at the marvel they had been privileged to see. They had indeed witnessed a spectacle not easily to be forgotten.'

The lifting of the bridge, *The Times* gushed, 'was imposing in the same sense as a great convulsion of the natural world; it was an exhibition of resistless force, which held the spectators spellbound and speechless'. A flotilla of ships then sailed through the bridge, led by the Harbour Master's vessel, *Daisy*. The gunboat HMS *Landrail* carried a band that played 'God Save the Queen' as it passed under the bridge. Hospitality was freely dispensed: some 1,200 people, including all those who had worked on the construction of the bridge, were entertained in marquees. The total number of attendees was believed to be over 3,000.

The Mazawattee tea company , which had a large warehouse immediately adjacent to the northern end of the bridge, cashed in on the event. It festooned its premises with patriotic bunting and issued a free souvenir booklet.

The bridge represented a marriage of architecture and engineering. From the time of its opening, it functioned as planned, but the 'purists' were, as predicted, critical. The architectural press was unforgiving in its reviews. This attitude was a reflection of the pervasive influence of the doctrine of 'truthfulness to materials' propagated by reformists including the critic John Ruskin and the designer and writer William Morris. *The Builder* condemned 'the many thousands spent on what is not the bridge at all, but an elaborate and costly make-believe'.[21] The towers were 'choice specimens of architectural gimcrack'. *Building News* too thought the bridge's architectural treatment a sham – 'no real art can tolerate a casing', it argued.[22]

One of the latter magazine's correspondents, Ellis Marsland, Honorary Secretary of the Society of Architects, was more outspoken.

The architect appears to have clothed the steel skeletons of the towers themselves with architectural skin and flesh, leaving the skeleton arms of the mid-river ones shaking hands with their smaller brethren on shore in all their bald and naked ugliness, giving one the impression that he had exhausted his resources when having to deal with these members.

ABOVE
Colour sketch by Andrew
Murray, the City Surveyor,
of the temporary pavilion
erected for the opening
ceremony of Tower Bridge.

The chains carrying the side spans were 'an eyesore'. The masonry
detailing was poor: 'the wall surface seems to be frittered away by
a multitude of tiny windows, and lacks dignity, repose, and depth'.
Marsland concluded that 'here was a splendid opportunity for
architecture to assert itself, but the opportunity has been lost, and
the engineer remains master of the situation'.[23]

Not that the engineering profession was entirely convinced by
the outcome of the architect/engineer collaboration. Some felt that
the bridge was overengineered and overdesigned, with a needlessly
complicated approach to providing a river crossing that generated many
questions. Why impede river traffic with two massive towers? What
use were the high-level walkways when the bridge opened and closed
in minutes and pedestrians would not use them? Was not the original
idea of an arch aesthetically preferable? At a meeting at the Institution
of Civil Engineers in 1897, Ewing Matheson, who had worked on an
alternative proposal with Rowland Mason Ordish, was scathing in
his comments:

> Temple Bar [the gate that had marked the entry point to the
> City from the west until its removal in 1878] was an interesting
> monument, but it had to be taken down as an obstruction, and
> he could not but think the day would come when the present
> Tower Bridge would likewise be removed.

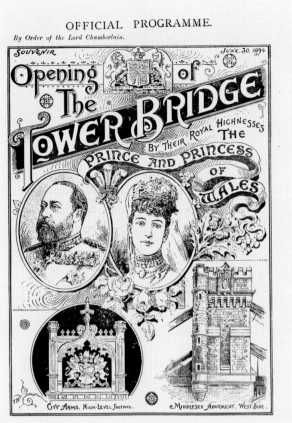

Matheson argued that the real need was for a railway bridge or one that carried both trains and road traffic as Newcastle's High Level Bridge did.

A senior member of the architectural profession, Arthur Beresford Pite (1861–1934), was more measured. He disliked 'the Gothic gimcrack of the granite casings of the towers, the ridiculous departure from faith and truth'. Yet the architecture of the bridge was, he conceded, 'an incident only, and a paltry one, compared with the greatness of the structure, its practical conquest of a difficult problem, and the overpowering expression of topsey-turveydom when the huge bascules lift and lower themselves as easily as a pair of hands'.[24] The architecture of the bridge was, in short, 'of no account' – Tower Bridge was an engineering triumph.

4 | TOWER BRIDGE IN OPERATION

THE BASIC PRINCIPLE underlying the design of Tower Bridge was hardly novel. Medieval drawbridges were raised and lowered over defensive moats, using hand-powered winches. Early examples of bascule bridges from about the eighteenth century used the same basic technology. They were more common in the Low Countries, with their many canals, than in Britain. Opening long, heavy spans constructed of iron or steel was, however, made possible only by the application of steam power: the technology that drove the first Industrial Revolution. Hydraulics were necessary for the smooth and efficient use of steam power on demand. It was hydraulic power that lifted – and still lifts (though now without steam) – the huge central leaves of Tower Bridge. Joseph Bramah (1748–1814), an inventor and locksmith, patented a hydraulic press in 1795.

BELOW
Sketch of Tower Bridge taken from a letter written by Henry Marc Brunel to his friend and business associate, the hydraulic engineer John George Gamble. It is dated 1 February 1885.

OPPOSITE
Section of the pump and cylinder of Joseph Bramah's hydraulic press, from the *Cyclopedia or Universal Dictionary* (1812) by Abraham Rees.

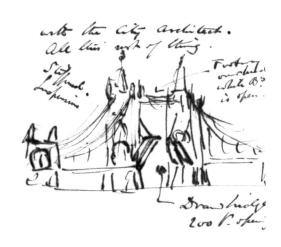

PRESS.

Mr. BRAMAH'S HYDROSTATIC PRESS.

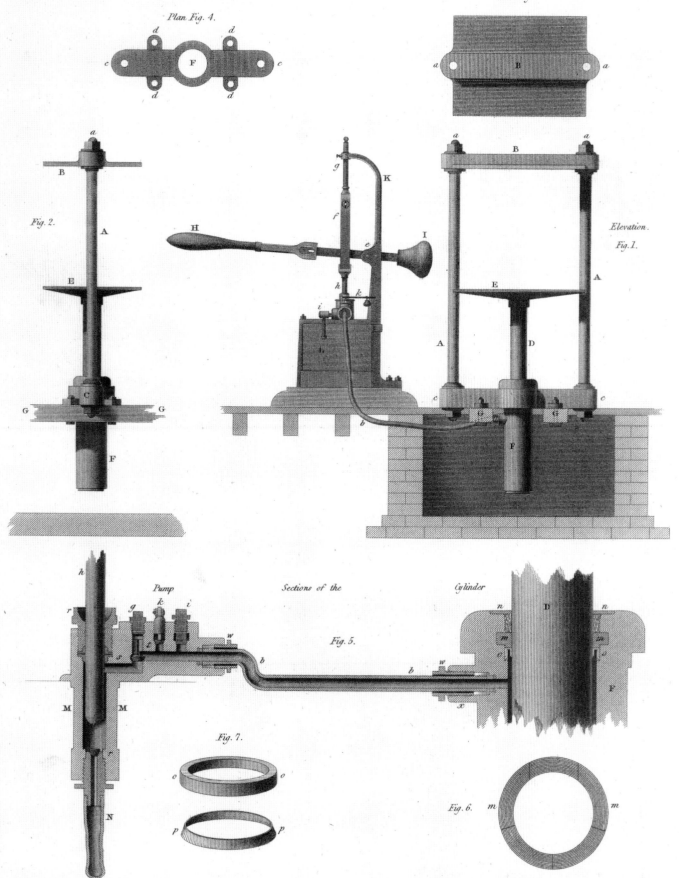

Plan Fig. 4.

Plan Fig. 3.

Fig. 2.

Elevation.

Fig. 1.

Sections of the   Cylinder

Pump

Fig. 5.

Fig. 7.

Fig. 6.

Published as the Act directs, 1812, by Longman, Hurst, Rees, Orme and Brown, Paternoster Row.

William Armstrong (1810–1900) was, however, the key pioneer in the development and widespread application of hydraulic power in Britain. He became one of the leading British industrialists of the Victorian era. Abandoning the legal career that his family had planned for him, Armstrong had begun to experiment with water power in the 1830s. By 1839 he had constructed a 'hydraulic engine' and demonstrated that water pressure could power the movement of a crane. Hydraulically powered cranes were the foundation of the company he established, with works at Elswick in his native Newcastle upon Tyne, in 1847. They were installed on the quays at Newcastle and at other ports. Soon Armstrong's company was building 100 such cranes a year.

Armstrong's next move was to develop an accumulator: basically, a large tank in which water was put under pressure by heavy weights, up to 1,500 lbs per square inch (10,342 kpa), to produce motive power as and when needed. A castellated accumulator tower was a prominent feature of the magnificent Albert Dock in Liverpool, designed by Jesse Hartley (1780–1860) and opened in 1845. The introduction of accumulators, storing the energy created by water under pressure, led to the widespread use of hydraulic power. A public hydraulic network began operating in Hull in 1876. Liverpool, Manchester and other cities soon followed. Hydraulic power came to London's docks in the 1850s, and the various dock companies established their own systems. The public system subsequently developed in London, and, extending across

BELOW LEFT
One of the hydraulic accumulators powering the movement of the bascules of Tower Bridge. Armstrong's invention of the accumulator made the widespread use of hydraulic power possible.

BELOW RIGHT
The accumulator house adjacent to the southern approach road to Tower Bridge. This building housed the two main hydraulic accumulators, supplemented by those in the towers. The chimney was for the boilers located in the engine house below.

much of the city, was operated by the London Hydraulic Power Company (established 1884). It laid 184 miles (296 km) of mains across the capital, with pumping stations at Wapping and Rotherhithe. Hydraulics powered most of the cranes as well as four swing bridges in London's docks, all powered by machinery built at Elswick. The Glasgow works of William Arrol, which fabricated the steelwork for Tower Bridge, made extensive use of hydraulic power, not least on the construction of the Forth Bridge.

Known as Sir W. G. Armstrong, Mitchell & Co. Ltd from 1882 – when Armstrong bought up the shipyard founded by Charles Mitchell – the company was to become a major shipbuilder and armaments manufacturer with a global reach. Armstrong was given a peerage in 1887. The ramblingly romantic Northumberland country house, Cragside, which he commissioned from the architect Richard Norman Shaw, boasted a hydraulic lift, electric lighting and central heating. The lighting was powered by hydroelectricity, of which Armstrong was also a pioneer.

In 1888 Sir W. G. Armstrong, Mitchell & Co. Ltd won the contract to provide the machinery to power Tower Bridge at an estimated cost of £85,232 (equivalent to over £5 million today). As part of his training as an engineer, Henry Marc Brunel, later the business partner of John Wolfe Barry, had spent some time as an apprentice at the Elswick works. It was Barry who was responsible for appointing Armstrong.

He recommended the company as having 'the greatest experience in the world in hydraulic machinery'.[1] The management of the Tower Bridge contract was given to Hamilton Rendel, brother of Stuart Rendel, who managed Armstrong's operations in London. The bridge was to have its own independent hydraulic system, powered by steam engines built at Elswick. If that were ever to fail the hydraulic system working throughout London's docklands could be used.

The two steam engines, which powered the bridge until the 1970s, were contained in an engine house beneath the southern approach road. Steam was generated by four massive coal-burning Lancashire boilers, each 30 ft (9 m) long and patented by Fairbairn of Manchester in 1844. Two were in use at any one time and they consumed 20 tons of coal weekly. (The coal was brought in by barge and conveyed from the wharf by trucks running on a narrow-gauge rail track. After the Second World War coal was delivered by road.) The engines powered hydraulic pumps, feeding water under pressure to two accumulators, 35 ft (10.5 m) high. These were placed close to the pumping engines, and there were two more in each of the towers, giving six in total. The accumulators were great cylinders, each fitted with a massive ram moving a heavy case of ballast. When power was used, for example to lift a crane, the ram dropped down the cylinder, rising again as water was pumped in. The function of the accumulators was to ensure that a constant pressure was maintained in the system and to store the output from the pumps

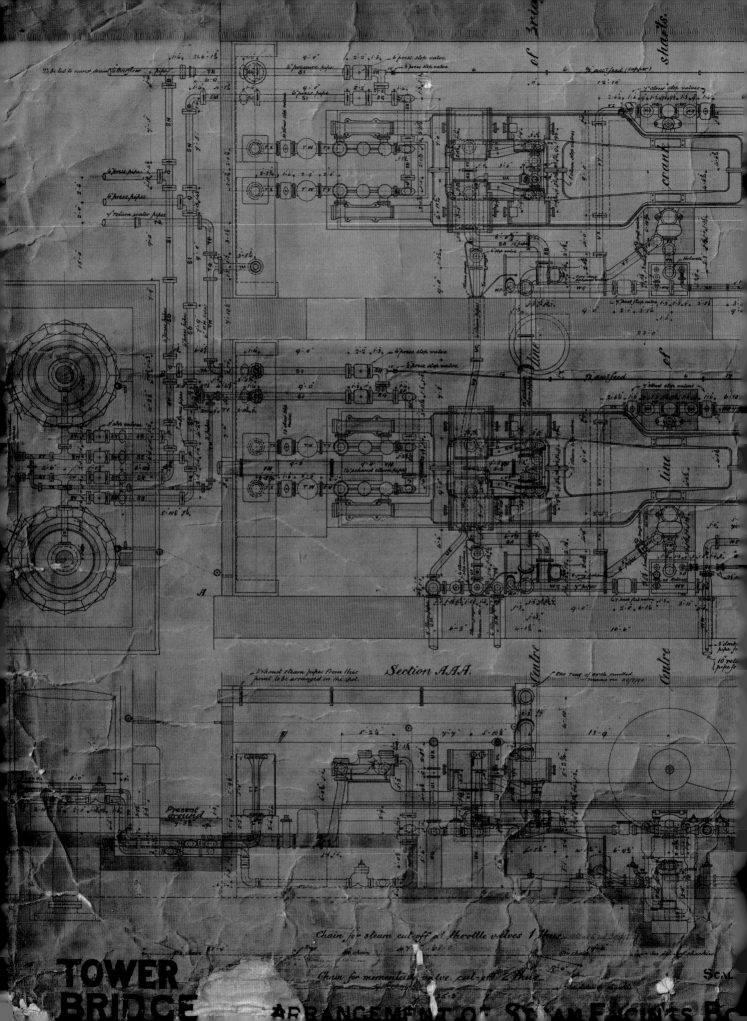

Section AAA.

TOWER
BRIDGE
ARRANGEMENT OF STEAM ENGINES

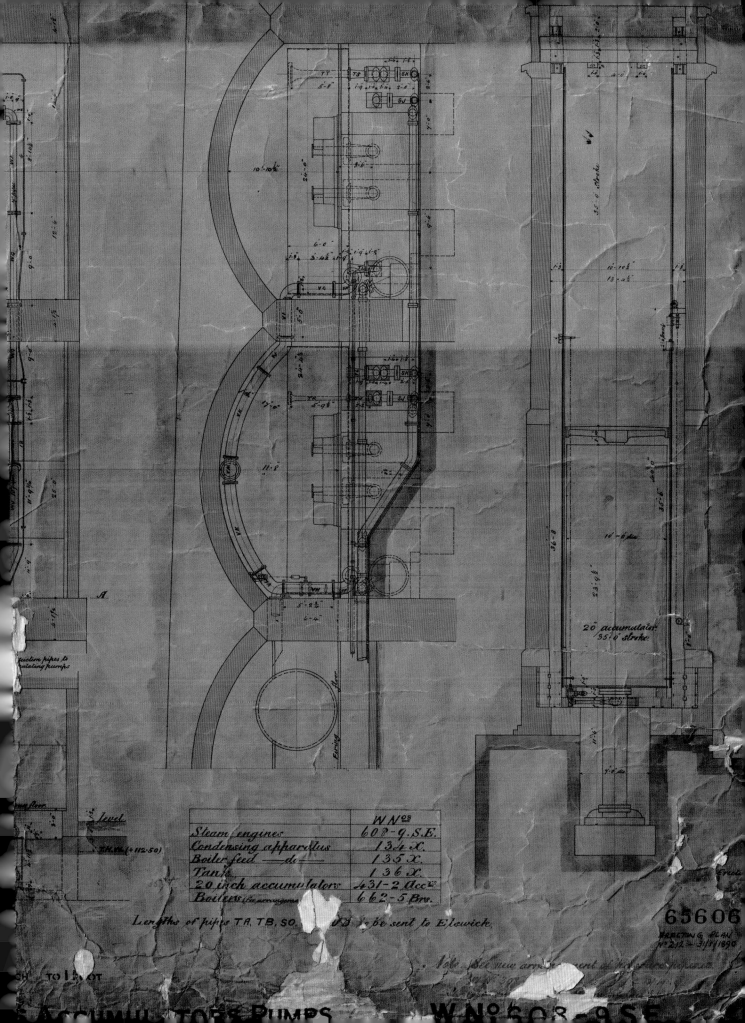

	W Nᵒˢ
Steam engines	608-9.S.E.
Condensing apparatus	134 X.
Boiler feed ——do——	135 X.
Tank	136 X.
20 inch accumulators	431-2 Accᵗ
Boilers (for accumulators)	662-5 Brs.

Lengths of pipes T.A. T.B. S.O. ... to be sent to Elswick.

65606

ERECTING PLAN
Nᵒ 212 — 31/12/1898

CH TO 1 FOOT

ACCUMULATOR PUMPS   W Nᵒ 608-9 S E

for use when the call came on demand to raise the bridge. Hydraulic pumps also fed water under high pressure from the accumulators to the lifting machinery. Waterpipes 6 in. (15 cm) in diameter ran up the south tower, along the high-level walkway and down the north tower.

The water pressure was 850 lbs per square inch (5,860 kpa), five times that generated by a typical steam locomotive. Each pier had two chambers containing the engines to drive the bascules, which could withstand the strongest winds. (Board of Trade regulations, imposed following the Tay Bridge disaster of 1879, stated that all new bridges had to be designed to withstand wind speeds of up to 90 miles per hour [149 kph]. These were unlikely to be experienced in the heart of London, however.) High-pressure water passed to the engines and drove pistons, turning cranks and moving geared wheels attached to pinion shafts running the width of the bridge. The shafts engaged with the cogwheels in the quadrants at the base of the bascules, which could be raised in just one minute. Not the least remarkable feature of the bridge was that the process of raising and lowering it was so smooth – and silent.

Despite the efficiency of the bridge's operations, there were calls as early as 1917 for modernization, such as conversion of the lifting mechanism to electric power. (William Sugg & Co.'s gas lamps remained in use until they were replaced by electric lighting in 1966.)

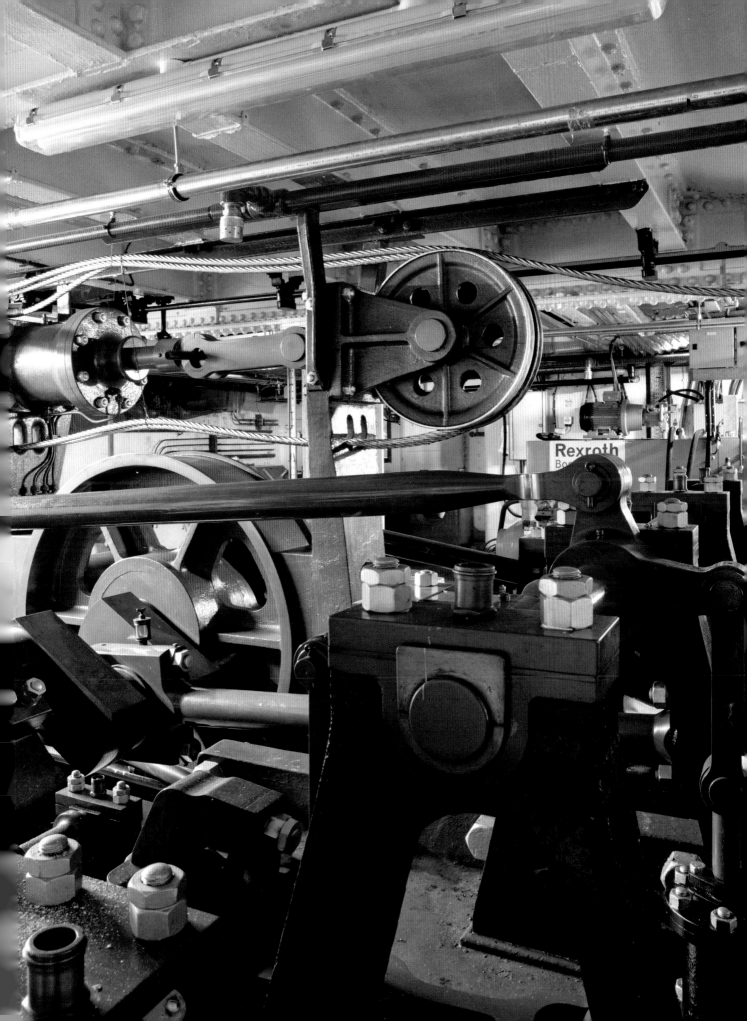

RAISING AND LOWERING THE BASCULES

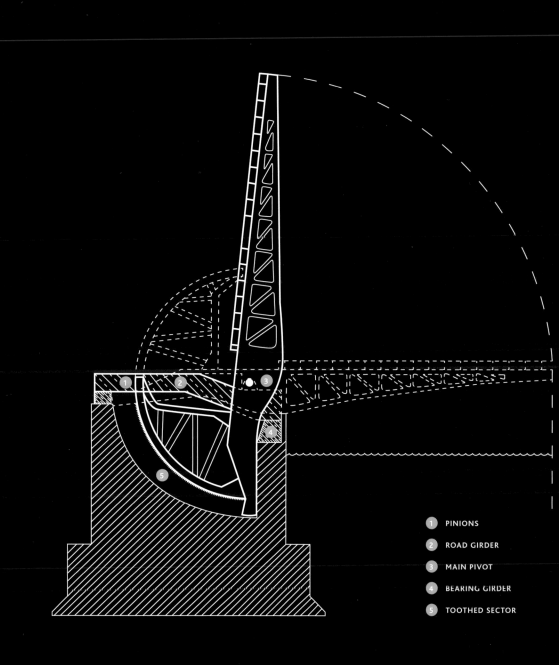

1. PINIONS
2. ROAD GIRDER
3. MAIN PIVOT
4. BEARING GIRDER
5. TOOTHED SECTOR

OPPOSITE
One of the huge
subterranean chambers
into which a bascule slides
when the bridge is opened.

ABOVE
Diagram detailing the
machinery involved in
raising and lowering each
of the bascules.

THE MACHINERY OF TOWER BRIDGE

Steam-powered hydraulic systems were originally used to lift and lower
the huge central leaves of Tower Bridge. These have now been replaced
by electrically powered units.

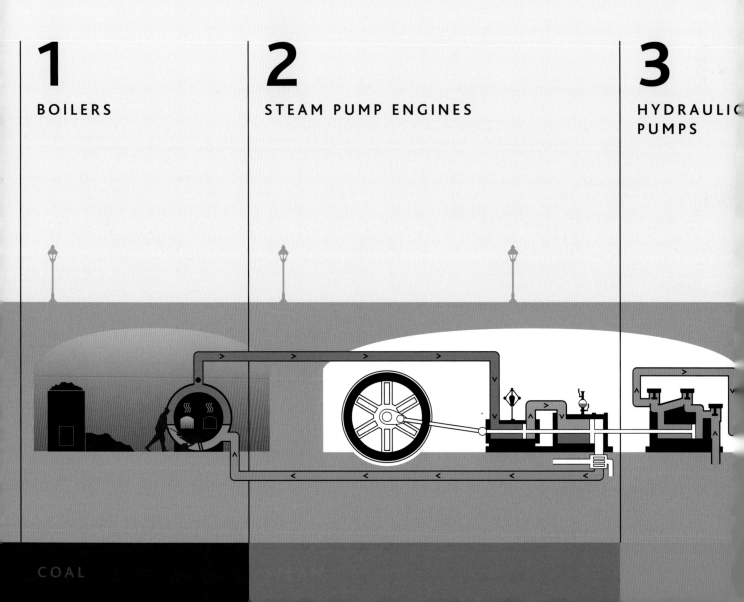

1
BOILERS

2
STEAM PUMP ENGINES

3
HYDRAULIC
PUMPS

COAL

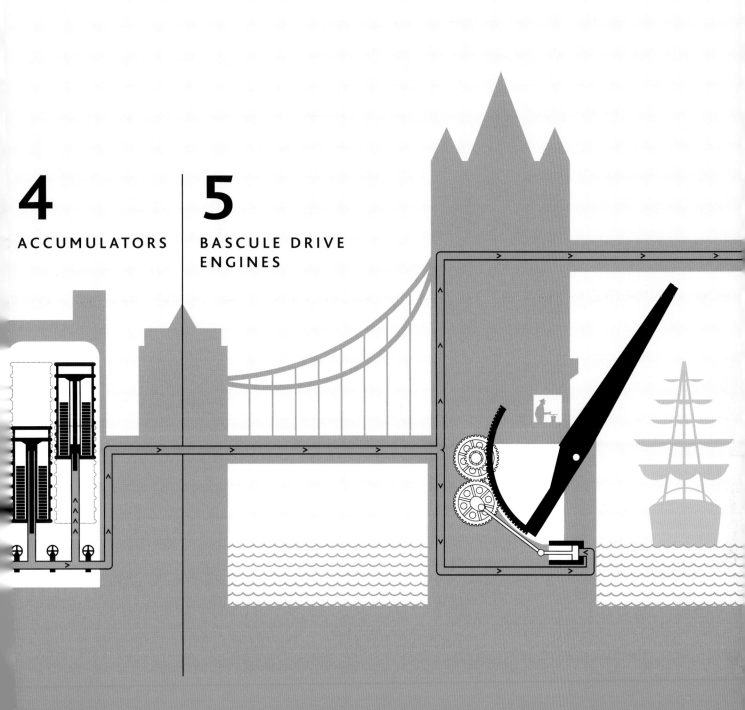

4
ACCUMULATORS

5
BASCULE DRIVE
ENGINES

But why change a system that worked so well? A report into the potential use of electric power was commissioned by the City Corporation from the engineer Sir Alexander Kennedy (1847–1928) and a 'Mr E. Cruttwell' – presumably George Edward Cruttwell. It concluded that while such a change would result in staffing levels being reduced – an important consideration during the First World War – the annual cost of running the bridge would be higher. Using electricity would mean that the bridge could be disabled by a power cut. The recommendation was to keep the steam engines in use.

By the 1960s the Pool of London was receiving fewer ships, as the larger vessels in service required deeper water at Tilbury and other docks. Some argued that the lifting mechanism could be abandoned and the bascules fixed in the closed position, making movement of road traffic smoother. In one month in 1894 the bridge was opened 655 times but by 1955 there were typically only 200 openings per month. The City, however, rejected this suggestion and decided to proceed with conversion to electric power. The installation of a new hydraulic system, using high-pressure oil rather than water, was connected to the existing lifting machinery. Electrical units built by Cleveland Bridge & Engineering Company powered the system. The existing steam engines and hydraulic system, with its network of connecting water pipes, were made redundant. Fortunately, although the need to ensure the smooth

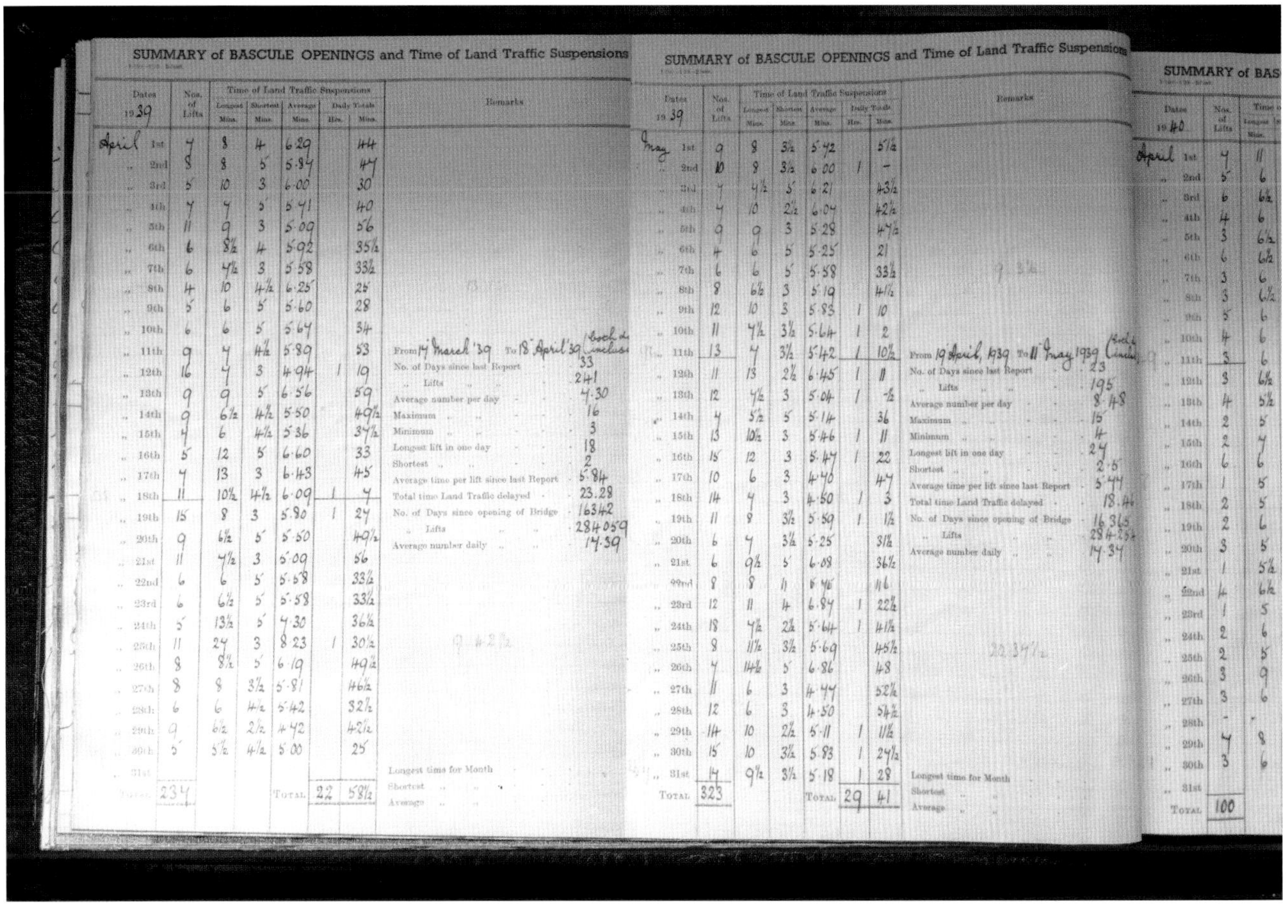

SUMMARY of BASCULE OPENINGS and Time of Land Traffic Suspensions

Dates 1939	No. of Lifts	Longest Mins.	Shortest Mins.	Average Mins.	Daily Totals Hrs.	Daily Totals Mins.	Remarks
April 1st	7	8	4	6.29		44	
„ 2nd	8	8	5	5.84		47	
„ 3rd	5	10	3	6.00		30	
„ 4th	7	7	3	6.41		40	
„ 5th	11	4	3	5.09		56	
„ 6th	6	8½	4	5.92		35½	
„ 7th	6	4½	3	5.58		33½	
„ 8th	4	10	4½	6.25		25	
„ 9th	5	6	5	5.60		28	
„ 10th	6	6	5	5.64		34	
„ 11th	9	7	4½	5.89		53	From 17 March '39 To 18 April '39 (Both days inclusive)
„ 12th	16	4	3	4.94		19	No. of Days since last Report ... 33
„ 13th	9	9	5	6.56		59	Lifts ... 241
„ 14th	9	6½	4½	5.50		49½	Average number per day ... 7.30
„ 15th	4	6	4½	5.36		34½	Maximum ... 16
„ 16th	5	12	5	6.60		33	Minimum ... 3
„ 17th	7	13	3	6.43		45	Longest lift in one day ... 18
„ 18th	11	10½	4½	6.09	1	7	Shortest ... 2
„ 19th	15	8	3	5.90	1	24	Average time per lift since last Report ... 5.84
„ 20th	9	6½	5	5.50		49½	Total time Land Traffic delayed ... 23.28
„ 21st	11	7½	3	5.09		56	No. of Days since opening of Bridge ... 16342
„ 22nd	6	6	5	5.58		33½	Lifts ... 284059
„ 23rd	6	6½	5	5.58		33½	Average number daily ... 14.39
„ 24th	11	13½	3	4.30		36½	
„ 25th	11	24	3	8.23	1	30½	
„ 26th	8	8½	5	6.19		49½	
„ 27th	8	8	3½	5.81		46½	
„ 28th	6	6	4½	5.42		32½	
„ 29th	9	6½	2½	4.42		42½	
„ 30th	5	3½	4½	5.00		25	
„ 31st							
Total	234				Total 22	53½	Longest time for Month / Shortest / Average

SUMMARY of BASCULE OPENINGS and Time of Land Traffic Suspensions

Dates 1939	No. of Lifts	Longest Mins.	Shortest Mins.	Average Mins.	Daily Totals Hrs.	Daily Totals Mins.	Remarks
May 1st	9	8	3½	5.42		5½	
„ 2nd	10	9	3½	6.00	1	-	
„ 3rd	7	4½	5	6.21		43½	
„ 4th	7	10	2½	6.04		42½	
„ 5th	5	9	3	5.28		47½	
„ 6th	4	8	5	5.25		21	
„ 7th	6	5	5	5.58		33½	
„ 8th	8	6½	5	5.19		41½	
„ 9th	12	10	3	5.83		10	
„ 10th	11	7½	3½	5.64	1	2	
„ 11th	13	7	3½	5.42		10½	From 19 April, 1939 To 11 May 1939 (Both days inclusive)
„ 12th	11	13	2½	6.45		11	No. of Days since last Report ... 23
„ 13th	12	4½	5	5.04		-½	Lifts ... 195
„ 14th	4	5½	5	5.14		36	Average number per day ... 8.48
„ 15th	13	10½	3	5.46		11	Maximum ... 15
„ 16th	15	12	3	5.47	1	22	Minimum ... 4
„ 17th	10	6	3	4.40		47	Longest lift in one day ... 24
„ 18th	14	4	3	4.50		1	Shortest ... 2.67
„ 19th	11	9	3½	5.89	1	1½	Average time per lift since last Report ... 5.44
„ 20th	6	4	3½	5.25		31½	Total time Land Traffic delayed ... 18.41
„ 21st	6	9½	5	6.09		36½	No. of Days since opening of Bridge ... 16365
„ 22nd	8	8	5	6.45		46	Lifts ... 284252
„ 23rd	12	11	4	6.84	1	22½	Average number daily ... 14.34
„ 24th	8	4½	3½	5.64	1	41½	
„ 25th	8	11½	3½	5.69		45½	
„ 26th	4	14½	5	6.86		48	
„ 27th	12	6	3	4.44		52½	
„ 28th	12	6	3	4.50		54½	
„ 29th	14	10	2½	5.11	1	11½	
„ 30th	15	10	3½	5.83	1	24½	
„ 31st	14	9½	3½	5.19	1	28	
Total	323				Total 29	41	Longest time for Month / Shortest / Average

SUMMARY of BASCULE OPENINGS ...

Dates 1940	No. of Lifts	Time ... Mins.
April 1st	7	11
„ 2nd	5	6
„ 3rd	6	6½
„ 4th	4	6
„ 5th	3	6½
„ 6th	3	6½
„ 7th	3	5
„ 8th	3	6½
„ 9th		
„ 10th	4	6
„ 11th	3	6
„ 12th	3	6½
„ 13th	4	5½
„ 14th	2	7
„ 15th	2	7
„ 16th	6	4
„ 17th	2	5
„ 18th	2	6
„ 19th	2	6
„ 20th	3	5½
„ 21st	4	5½
„ 22nd	4	6½
„ 23rd	2	6
„ 24th	2	6
„ 25th	3	9
„ 26th	3	9
„ 27th	3	6
„ 28th	2	8
„ 29th	4	8
„ 30th	3	6
„ 31st		
Total	100	

OPPOSITE
One of the Lancashire
boilers that powered the
machinery of Tower Bridge
for nearly eighty years.

BELOW LEFT
The walkways during the
final stages of completion.

BELOW RIGHT
The pedestrian walkways
were little used and in
1910 were closed – not to
be reopened for another
seventy years.

working of the bridge in the future was the first priority, the historic significance of its original machinery was recognized. Two steam engines and four bascule drive engines were retained in situ as part of the modernization programme, which began in 1972.

The potential of Tower Bridge as a visitor attraction was clear, but much needed to be done to make it accessible. The high-level pedestrian walkways, always underused, had been closed to the public in 1910. During the Second World War they had been stripped of their decorative ironwork, which was sent for scrap, and their roofs had been removed.

In 1894–95, its first year of operation, the bridge was raised more than 6,000 times – on average 17 times a day – and on a typical day up to 8,000 vehicles and 60,000 pedestrians crossed it. The passenger lifts in each tower, holding up to 25 people, were hydraulically powered. In practice, most pedestrians preferred to wait some minutes while the bridge was raised and lowered. (When, on occasions, a number of ships passed through in quick succession, the wait could be up to half an hour.) By 1896 the lifts were generally out of operation, so that the energetic and impatient had to climb 206 steps at one end and descend another 206 at the other.

From the start river traffic had priority (a rule that still applies) and any vessel needing clear passage could request that the bridge be opened; today twenty-four hours' notice is required. A signalling system similar to that on railways operated, with semaphore flags in daytime and coloured lights after dark. A back-up audible system based on Morse code was used in poor visibility. The working of the bridge was controlled from cabins at either end. Each was responsible for one bascule, the south usually opening first. A telephone system installed by Spagnoletti & Crookes allowed for instant communication.

Despite the sophistication of its mechanics, Tower Bridge when first opened required a staff of eighty. They included engine drivers, signalmen, watchmen, and fire service and police contingents (see Chapter 6). A resident engineer was responsible for the smooth operation of the bridge, and was backed up by a thirty-strong maintenance staff to keep everything in working order. Overall management of the bridge was entrusted to the Bridge Master. Like the Resident Engineer he was required to live on site. The bridge was staffed day and night. All contingencies were provided for, but there were few emergencies. J. E. Tuit reckoned that the bridge's annual operating cost was about £3,500. About half of this amount was the expense of running the machinery – the coal bill for the boilers powering the bascules was a sizeable element.

BELOW
Cars, cyclists and pedestrians wait to cross Tower Bridge in 1933.

OPPOSITE
An electrically powered indicator, resembling a railway signal, for use when the bridge opened. Colour drawing from an engineering plan produced by the office of Sir John Wolfe Barry, 25 May 1894.

OVERLEAF
Sunset over the Upper Pool seen from Tower Bridge, in a 1920s photograph by George Davison Reid. The control box on the right operated the semaphore signals and lamps that controlled the passage of ships through the bridge.

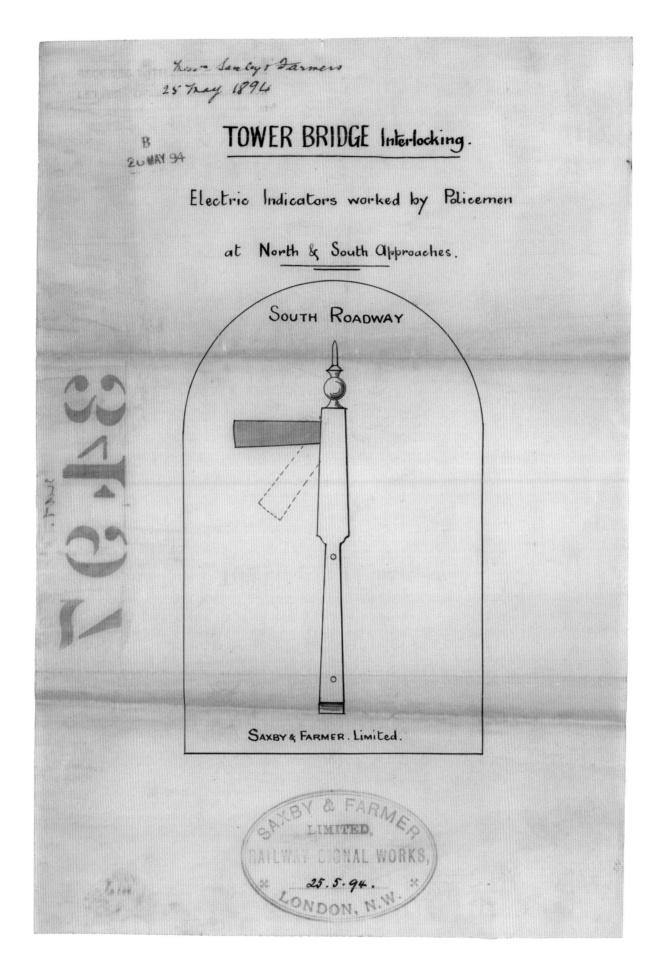

Messrs. Saxby & Farmers
25 May 1894

B
20 MAY 94

TOWER BRIDGE Interlocking.

Electric Indicators worked by Policemen

at North & South Approaches.

SOUTH ROADWAY

SAXBY & FARMER. Limited.

SAXBY & FARMER
LIMITED,
RAILWAY SIGNAL WORKS,
25.5.94.
LONDON, N.W.

OPPOSITE

The preserved interior
of the control cabin on
the south side of the
bridge, with levers, much
like those in a railway
signal box, for raising and
lowering the bascules.

BELOW LEFT

Detail of a brass dial in
the bridge control cabin.

BELOW RIGHT

The simple modern control
panel for opening and
closing the bridge.

OVERLEAF

The bascules being raised –
one of the great sights
of London.

A century and a quarter after its completion, Tower Bridge continues to operate as efficiently as it did when new. The central span is now lifted by the touch of buttons, rather than by pulling levers similar to those in railway signal boxes. Electricity, rather than steam, powers the hydraulic system. Yet the principal working parts of the bridge remain unchanged. To see the bridge raised and lowered – usually now to allow the passage of a pleasure boat – is one of the defining sights of London.

5 | AN ICON OF LONDON

OPPOSITE
This sequence of photographs looking north-east shows the raising and lowering of the bascules to allow the pleasure boat *Dixie Queen* to pass through the bridge.

'THE TOWER BRIDGE IS, on a first sight, infinitely more astonishing to the sight seer than any other London monument', wrote Mrs E. T. Cook in *Highways and Byways in London* (1902). 'It has a medieval look, as of some gigantic fortress of the sixteenth century', she continued approvingly. The French writer Gabriel Mourey was equally impressed, seeing the bridge as a perfect fusion of engineering and architecture. He wrote that 'all the audacity of the modern architects, which is to create the works of the future, here bursts forth, suspended on the heavy foundations of the past; with so much measure and proportion that nothing offends in the medley of archaism and modernity'.[1] Achieving this balance, Mourey believed, was a reflection of British character.

For others the marriage of architecture and engineering at Tower
Bridge was not a happy one. The critic A. Trystan Edwards (best
known for his 1924 book, *Good and Bad Manners in Architecture*) wrote
in 1925: 'the medievalists won the day, and although the decision to
clothe the towers with stone was right, it was arrived at for the wrong
reasons, for it was a contempt for steelwork in general rather than
a regard for civic architecture that influenced their judgement.'[2]
Lecturing at Liverpool University in 1945 the architect and critic
H. S. Goodhart-Rendel (1887–1959) spoke of the 'inconsistency found
in many buildings designed by engineers and trimmed afterwards by
hireling ornamenters'.[3] He considered that Tower Bridge 'was quite
good in the engineering stage, but, as it developed into architecture,
it took the wrong turning'. Coincidentally he was the grandson of
Stuart Rendel, Lord Rendel (1834–1913), sometime partner in
Sir W. G. Armstrong, Mitchell & Co. Ltd.

Writing twenty years later, the architectural critic Ian Nairn (1930–83)
was more forgiving: 'In daylight, the romantic aspirations never get off
the ground', he wrote. 'But at night it is magnificent. Intermittently lit,
tremendously bulky, the pompous trimmings concealed and the huge
suspending cables emphasized....'[4] More recently, the writer Peter
Ackroyd has conceded that Tower Bridge 'was an extraordinary feat
of engineering', but felt that it seemed 'deliberately to have been built
on an impersonal and somewhat forbidding scale'.[5]

BELOW
View in 2018 from the
upper walkway, looking
upstream across the Tower
of London towards the
forest of office towers in
the City.

Yet it was because of its size and its architectural form, the architect, sculptor and writer Theo Crosby (1925–94) argued in 1970, that the bridge was so successful. It produces 'an effect on its surroundings infinitely greater than its elemental function as a traffic machine'. The bridge, like Charles Garnier's Paris Opera and the tragically lost Pennsylvania Station in New York, was a 'necessary monument'. It was 'still a place to walk on: it invites a crossing by its promise of a complex architectural experience, its promise of something shared: a marvellous series of views up and down stream, participation in the working life of the river…and an involvement in the drama of the Pool'.[6] The river has ceased to be a place of work and the Pool is now devoid of cargo ships and lighters, but Crosby's words still ring true.

Doctrinaire modernists, committed to the gospel of functionalism, might never love Tower Bridge. But the architect Terry Farrell, a pioneer of Postmodernism in Britain, did not share their prejudices. It was, he wrote, 'the most recognisable symbol for London; an extraordinary concoction of Englishness and of Victorian quirky historicism…. Designed in the spirit of its outer historical clothing, it is a work of brilliant engineering innovation.'[7] As Ken Allinson has commented in *Architects and Architecture of London*, 'one surely has to be tired of architecture not to enjoy its theatricality'.[8]

Architects, engineers and critics might disagree on the merits of Tower Bridge, but it quickly became an iconic sight of London. It has

Quel plaisir à Louvres.

Maurice Ghose

Tower Bridge, London

been reproduced on countless postcards and photographed by millions of tourists. In 1912 it was the scene for a daring stunt by the aviator Frank McLean, who flew his biplane between the bascules and the high-level walkway. He received a ticking off but after the stunt was repeated by the Australian Sidney Pickles in 1919, flying through the bridge was made illegal. This did not deter others. The last, and most spectacular, incident took place in 1968 when the Royal Air Force pilot Alan Pollock flew a Hawker Hunter jet through the bridge. He was arrested and dismissed from the service on mental health grounds.

Tower Bridge survived the Great War of 1914–18 unscathed. In an era when Victorian architecture was increasingly despised, an overhaul of the disused high-level walkways in the 1930s saw most of the ornamental ironwork sold for scrap. During the Second World War, German bombing devastated much of the City of London and the docks. In 1941 a bomb damaged the span on the south shore and destroyed an adjacent tug. Repairs were carried out quickly and the bridge stayed open. To 'progressive' minds, the bridge seemed an over-elaborate Victorian relic. In 1943 W. F. C. Holden (1882–1953), Chief Architect to the National Provincial Bank (not to be confused with Charles Holden, the famed architect of 1930s London Underground stations), put forward a proposal for a radical makeover. The bridge would be transformed into the 'Crystal Tower Bridge'. The bascules would be retained but the towers and high-level walkways

would be rebuilt to contain 200,000 sq. ft (18,000 sq. m) of office space. This scheme would generate income and vastly reduce the cost of maintenance. The Bridge House Estates Committee noted the proposal as practical but adjourned further consideration of it. It progressed no further.

The postwar years saw a slow but steady decline in the trade of the Pool of London. The bridge opened less often and by the 1960s it was no longer possible for a ship to get the bascules lifted on demand – from 1962, twenty-four hours' notice had to be given, the rule that applies to this day. There were suggestions that it would soon be possible to permanently close the central span and abandon the lifting mechanism, which in any case needed updating. By the 1960s Britain's railways were being rapidly modernized, with steam locomotives replaced by diesel power. In 1970 the City Corporation resolved to fund a major upgrade scheme, including the replacement of steam power by electricity. Electric engines were brought into use from 1972, with two units at each corner of the bridge. When the bridge was new no chances had been taken with the power supply – the steam engines supplied twice the power needed to raise the central span, so that one engine could always be held in reserve. The new electrical units equally provided standby power 100% in excess of what was required for lifting.

Tower Bridge was one of the sights of London from the time of its completion. But the idea of making it a visitor attraction, accessible to the public, emerged only in the 1970s. It had been given protection as a listed building as early as 1949 but in 1973 its status was upgraded to Grade I. This places it alongside St Paul's Cathedral and the Palace of Westminster as a structure of exceptional significance. Consultants were appointed to devise a strategy for opening up the bridge, providing a safe and convenient route for visitors while minimizing changes to its fabric. The need for quite substantial repairs was soon identified, with areas of the stonework in need of consolidation or replacement. New weight limits were imposed on vehicles crossing the bridge. As part of the celebrations for Her Majesty Queen Elizabeth II's Silver Jubilee in 1977 the bridge was repainted in red, white and blue, to the annoyance of purists who wanted the wartime battleship grey retained.

The opening of Tower Bridge as a visitor attraction in 1982 was one element in a wholesale transformation of London's riverside. From the mid-1960s on all of London's docks were progressively abandoned. The Royal Docks to the east were the last to close in 1981 and all shipping trade moved to Tilbury in Essex. The historic London Docks complex of Wapping was entirely destroyed in the 1970s, its warehouses demolished – a tragic waste – and dock basins filled in.

ABOVE
One of the redundant steam pumping engines was removed in the 1970s and is now housed in the Forncett Industrial Steam Museum in Norfolk.

OPPOSITE
Abseiling workers carry out maintenance repairs on the bridge in 2012.

OVERLEAF
Close-up view of the north side of the bridge in 2018, with the open bascules seen on the left.

St Katharine Docks, adjacent to Tower Bridge, fared rather better after its closure in 1968. Although most of its buildings were lost – some of the warehouses had been destroyed by wartime bombs – the dock basins were retained. They formed the basis for a mixed-use development including a large (and overbearing) hotel, bars, restaurants and housing. On the south side of the river Hay's Dock was infilled. However, its warehouses were converted to shops, offices and housing, with a steel and glass galleria as the centrepiece of the development.

Close by, the veteran Royal Navy light cruiser HMS *Belfast* found a final berth in 1971 and soon became a major visitor attraction. Immediately downstream of Tower Bridge, Butler's Wharf, closed in 1972, was similarly reborn as a fashionable residential and leisure complex. There the Anchor Brewhouse (closed in 1982) and the warehouses along Shad Thames were converted to offices and flats, with restaurants along the riverside. More recently the area to the west of the bridge has re-emerged as London Bridge City (also known as More London). This area contains offices, restaurants, the new Bridge Theatre and London's City Hall (the offices of the Mayor of London and the London Assembly). Tower Bridge is now at the heart of a dynamically regenerated, but entirely postindustrial urban quarter that straddles the Thames.

The 1970s modernization programme re-equipped the bridge as a working river crossing. But there was a recognition that it was equally a historic artefact of enormous interest. The decision was taken to retain two of the Armstrong steam pumping engines and four of the bascule drive engines. The engine room on the south side of the bridge is a key part of the visitor experience. The visitor attraction is entered via a glass pavilion at the base of the north-west tower. It houses the ticket office and was designed by bere:architects. It was opened in 1993 in preparation for the bridge's centenary the following year. The pavilion's minimal aesthetic is an appropriate contrast to the massive masonry abutment of the bridge above.

The most spectacular feature of the Tower Bridge experience – attracting more than 800,000 paying visitors a year – is the thrill of crossing the high-level walkways. These were reopened in 1982 after major restoration work. This involved the reinstatement of the roofs, the glazing-in of the sides and the replacement of the decorative cast-iron work removed during the Second World War, albeit using glass-reinforced plastic replicas. In 2014 a new dimension was added to this experience when sections of glass flooring – seven layers deep and with stomach-churning views down to the roadway and river – were inserted.

BELOW LEFT
A view up to the pedestrian walkways. These were reopened to the public in 1982 and are now part of the visitor experience of Tower Bridge.

BELOW RIGHT
Glass floors in the walkways provide vertiginous views down to the road below.

OPPOSITE
The bridge seen from a tourist boat in 2016. The ticket office is a minimal steel and glass structure, and is designed to contrast with the solidity of the Victorian architecture.

A new lighting system was installed in 2012, in time for the Queen's Diamond Jubilee and the opening of the Olympic and Paralympic Games in London. It allowed the bridge to be transformed at night – when a Great Britain team member won a gold medal in the 2012 Games, for example, it turned the same dazzling colour. The lights were used to mark the births of royal babies. The bridge was lit blue to announce the arrival of Prince George in 2013 and Prince Louis in 2018, and pink for their sister, Princess Charlotte, in 2015.

In the century and a quarter since its completion, Tower Bridge has managed to avoid many of the misfortunes that have befallen London. It was, however, almost the scene of a terrible accident in December 1952, when the northern bascule began to open as a number 78 bus was crossing. The relief watchman, it seems, had failed to operate the warning lights but the driver, Albert Gunter, managed to land the bus upright on the bascule. He suffered a broken leg, and the passengers and bus conductor no more than minor injuries.

In 1997 US President Bill Clinton, accompanied by the UK Prime Minister Tony Blair, suffered the indignity of being held on the south side of the bridge, to the alarm of his security team, when a booked 'lift' began. The technical officer in charge, Glen Ellis, rightly pointed out that he had had no warning of the motorcade's approach and that, in any case, the law stated that river traffic always has priority.

Tower Bridge today, as it did in 1894, remains a gateway to the City. While the area of Southwark on its south side is no longer the warren of wharves, warehouses and slum housing it was in the Victorian age, the bridge remains a dramatic marker on the north side of the transition from City to East End. The debate about the need for a bridge, or any kind of river crossing adjacent to the Tower, was lengthy. London might have had a very different bridge on this site, or even a tunnel. Had the debate extended into the twentieth century, the bridge might not have been built, at least in its present form, as the port of London moved ever further downstream and the trade of the old wharves diminished. The memorable form of the bridge was generated by vested interests: the need to maintain the historic Pool of London as a working port while creating a convenient river crossing. After years of indecision it was Horace Jones who produced a practical solution to the problem. But it was John Wolfe Barry who turned an idea into a buildable scheme. As an architect–engineer collaboration, the project prefigured the Millennium Bridge, opened in 2000, which, after some teething troubles were resolved, has itself become a popular London icon.

Tower Bridge is a great feat of engineering, but it is equally a great work of architecture, thanks to the vision of Barry and the skill of George Daniel Stevenson. The former conceded the case for an 'aesthetical' treatment of the basic structure. The latter developed an architectural vocabulary that, while paying its respects to the Tower of London, is inventive and highly individual, a late flowering of the Gothic Revival at a time when that movement seemed defunct.

The bridge may have looked back to the Middle Ages for architectural inspiration, but in so many other respects it looked forwards to the twentieth century. A major element in the success of the project was the degree to which prefabrication was used for the superstructure. It was hardly a new development: a 'kit of parts' strategy had been fundamental to the success of the Crystal Palace, built for the Great Exhibition in London of 1851. Similarly, as early as 1796 the first Wear Bridge in Sunderland had been constructed of pre-assembled components.

But Tower Bridge is, in effect, a machine as well as a structure. Its construction involved close coordination between engineers, steelwork manufacturers in Scotland and the Armstrong works in Newcastle upon Tyne, responsible for the working parts of the bridge. Similar thinking underpinned High-tech projects of the mid- to late twentieth century such as Paris's Centre Pompidou and London's Lloyd's Building, large elements of which were assembled offsite.

Bridges define cities: Sydney's Harbour Bridge, New York's Brooklyn Bridge and San Francisco's Golden Gate Bridge may exceed Tower Bridge in scale but it ranks alongside all of them as a symbol of a great city. Completed in the last decade of Queen Victoria's reign, it has seen the City devastated by war and transformed by redevelopment. The Thames now carries pleasure boats for visitors rather than cargo-laden ships. Tower Bridge is one constant in an ever-changing urban scene, a means of crossing the river but even more an object of fascination and delight.

6 | THE WORKERS OF TOWER BRIDGE

CLOTHED IN IMPERMEABLE granite and
seemingly as impregnable and immovable as its
neighbour the Tower of London, Tower Bridge is
both an imposing work of architecture and a huge,
complex piece of working machinery. It has always
required an expert team to maintain and operate it.
Into the second half of the twentieth century, the
bridge's smooth operation was vital for the working
of the Pool of London, a destination for cargoes
arriving in the capital. Today the cargo ships and
lighters have gone, along with most of the warehouses
and wharves. But the task of maintaining the bridge,
now a major visitor attraction, remains, and the
City of London's Bridge House Estates is still
responsible for what is now a venerable piece of
Victorian engineering.

ABOVE
Workmen involved in the
building of Tower Bridge
pose for a group portrait,
January 1890.

If Tower Bridge, as a great machine, resembles an ocean-going ship, its captain is the Bridge Master. Not surprisingly, a number of those who have served in this role have had a naval background. The first of them was Bertie Angelo Cator, appointed Bridge Master on the opening of the bridge in 1894. But for Cator, it seems, the call of the sea was strong and he returned to the Royal Navy within little more than a year. His successor, Richard Wakeham Roberts, had served as a captain in the Merchant Navy, mostly on sailing ships, before being appointed as Cator's deputy in 1894.

John Gass was, in contrast, an engineer, who had been a senior member of the Armstrong, Mitchell & Co. team working on the installation of the bridge's hydraulic system. Gass occupied the office of Superintendent Engineer from 1896, becoming Bridge Master in 1917 and retiring in 1930 at the age of seventy-eight. Gass was succeeded by another sailor, John Buchanan, originally an officer in the Merchant Navy, but with a distinguished career in the Royal Navy in the First World War. Leslie Priestley, Bridge Master from 1936 to 1959, was in office when, in 1952, the number 78 bus 'jumped' the bridge as it began to open (see Chapter 5). A press report recorded that he rapidly appeared on the scene, smartly dressed in overcoat and bowler hat. The naval tradition was maintained by Anthony Rabbit, who retired as Bridge Master in 1985. He had been in office for the reopening of the bridge, following a major restoration, in 1982. For the occasion,

Commander Anthony
Rabbit, Bridge Master, and
members of his team, July
1982. They are dressed
in Victorian uniforms,
probably for the reopening
of Tower Bridge that year.
Commander Rabbit retired
in 1985.

he sported a version of the uniform that his predecessor had worn
at the opening ceremony in 1894. The last Bridge Master was Eric
Sutherns, who retired in 2012, following the London Olympics and
the Queen's Diamond Jubilee. Since then members of the Corporation
of London have stepped in to fill the role for ceremonial purposes.

The office of Bridge Master was a highly responsible one and was
correspondingly well paid. The £380 starting salary received by John
Gass, rising to £750 by the time of his retirement, was supplemented by
free accommodation in the Master's House. This building, completed
in 1912 on the southern approach, replaced a residence in one of the
abutment towers. The Bridge Master was responsible:

> for the maintenance of the Bridge approaches and machinery, and
> for the safe and efficient working of the same. To receive the money
> and to pay the wages to the staff, order the stores and materials
> required. Make any necessary drawings, examine and certify
> the accounts. To make and submit to the Bridge House Estates
> Committee a monthly report as to the working of the Bridge,
> also an annual report with costs of maintenance of the same and
> to attend the meetings and carry out the orders of the Bridge House
> Estates Committee.[1]

The staff of up to 100 working on the bridge in the decades after its
opening in 1894 included a wide variety of trades and skills. Many of
those employed were born and lived within a few miles of the bridge,
in Bermondsey to the east. One section of the workforce, headed by
the Senior Head Watchman, was responsible for the regulation of
road and river traffic. Charles Cranbrook, ex-Royal Navy, who took
up the post of Senior Head Watchman in 1900, was given free
accommodation on site and a free domestic gas supply in addition
to a salary of £1 16s. a week. The chain of command then descended
to the Head Watchman, who would alternate night shifts with the
Senior Head Watchman – the bridge never slept.

The Senior Head Watchman was also responsible for overseeing the
bridge when the Bridge Master was absent. Edwin Boyd, appointed
to the position in 1909, was another sailor. He had ten years' service in
the Royal Navy before he came to Tower Bridge as a gateman in 1897.
Signalmen and watchmen controlled the passage of ships through
the bridge, working from cabins in both towers, while gatemen were
responsible for stopping road and pedestrian traffic when the bridge
was opened to vessels. For many years the bridge kept its own team
of horses, stabled under the southern approach – occasionally horses
dropped dead while hauling carts across the bridge and in such an
event assistance was at hand.

Another group of workers controlled the opening and closing of
the bridge. The fundamental element in the operation of the bridge
was steam power, which drove the hydraulic machinery that lifted the
leaves of the central span. The Lancashire boilers had to be constantly
fed with coal and maintained to a high standard. The job description
for stokers notes that they were 'to attend to the boilers, keep up steam,
attend to the water, trim and wheel coals into boiler rooms, clean out
the boilers, furnaces and flues, and keep the boilers and boiler rooms
clean'. They were also required to assist the pumping engine drivers
'in overhauling, repairing and keeping the gear in order and clean and
to do any other work or work overtime if considered necessary'.[2]

It was backbreaking work: shovelling 20 tons of coal a week in a
hot, dirty atmosphere. Long shifts day and night were needed to
ensure that the bridge could always open on request. The weekly pay
of a stoker in 1900 was £1 10s., considered a good wage at the time.
In view of the conditions, many stokers took up opportunities to escape
the boiler room to become bridge drivers, who were responsible for
opening and closing the bascules.

A large maintenance team of up to thirty men, headed by the
Superintendent Engineer, ensured that the bridge was kept in
working order and pristine condition. It included gas and water fitters,
blacksmiths, bricklayers, carpenters, painters, plumbers, oilers, and
general navvies and handymen. One of the fitters was responsible for
lighting, extinguishing and cleaning the gas lamps that lined the bridge.
A workshop block at the south-west end of the bridge was completed
in 1895 and had its own power supply provided by a single cylinder
steam engine.

A small clerical department that dealt with wages and other
payments employed timekeepers and storekeepers as well as general
office clerks. Conspicuously absent, even in this area of work – at least
until the interwar years – were women employees. One exception was
Hannah Griggs, employed for a decade or more as a cook. She had
been born in 1888 to a single mother in Bermondsey, joined the bridge
staff in 1902 and stayed about ten years, working, it is assumed, for the
Bridge Master. John Gass's daughter Laura was employed as a tracer,
preparing working drawings, in the small office attached to the
workshop block.

The First World War saw staff levels reduced – some less arduous jobs were temporarily carried out by disabled servicemen – but even by 1938 there were still eighty-four people employed on the bridge. This total was reduced only slightly over the next forty years. In more recent years staff numbers have decreased but in return new posts have been created. The biggest reduction in staffing was due to the move from coal to electric power in 1976. A more efficient system meant that stokers and labourers were no longer needed. At the same time the rules for opening the bridge were changed, requiring a ship to give at least twenty-four hours' notice of a lift. This meant that staffing could be planned and scheduled as required.

But the task of keeping the bridge a working monument continues. Since the bridge first opened as a visitor attraction in 1982 – it now attracts about 800,000 visitors a year – staff have been recruited to sell tickets, greet the public, and look after marketing, education programmes and corporate events. Security officers have the task of keeping the bridge a safe and welcoming environment. Technical officers keep it in perfect working order – the post of bridge driver still exists. Today ninety-seven people have permanent jobs at Tower Bridge, with others drafted in to provide support at busy times. The income generated by tourism provides a return to the City Bridge Trust, which supports charitable works in inner London boroughs.

LEFT
A bridge employee,
possibly Jo Tapper,
surveying traffic from
a control cabin.

OPPOSITE
An unidentified Port of
London official operates
the hydraulic engines
that raise and lower the
bascules of Tower Bridge.
Photograph of c. 1950.

OVERLEAF
Bridge foreman Stanley
Fletcher stands beside one
of the original Victorian
steam pumping engines,
which was announced for
sale that year (1976). He
was the longest serving
employee at the time.

For a century and a quarter Tower Bridge has adapted and
reinvented itself just as London has done. It has seen two world wars,
the decline of traditional industries, national celebrations and national
tragedies. Today it is an icon of London, the global city, a symbol of
stability and continuity in a changing world, loved by Londoners and
by countless others worldwide.

FACTS AND FIGURES

When it was built, Tower Bridge was the largest and most sophisticated bascule bridge ever completed. The facts and figures below demonstrate what an extraordinary undertaking it represented:

- Length of each side span: 82.3 m (270 ft)
- Length of central span: 60.9 m (200 ft)
- Depth of the foundations into the river bed: 7.9 m (26 ft)
- Number of bricks used: 31,000,000
- Weight of steel used: 10,886 tonnes (12,000 tons)
- Weight of iron used: 1,088 tonnes (1,200 tons)
- Weight of each bascule (including counterweight): 1,088 tonnes (1,200 tons)
- Weight of each chain: 1 tonne per 30 cm (1 ton per foot)
- Composition of the bascule counterweight: 263.8 tonnes (290 tons) of lead, plus 54.4 tonnes (60 tons) of cast iron
- Height of the walkways above the roadway: 33.5 m (110 ft)
- Height of the bridge from the road to the foundations: 27.4 m (90 ft)
- Length of each walkway: 70.1 m (230 ft)
- Tensile strength of the steel used: 4,170–4,942 bars (27–32 tons per sq. in.)
- Amount of granite and stone used: 6,654 m³ (235,000 ft³)
- Amount of cement used: 18,143 tonnes (20,000 tons)
- Estimated number of rivets used in construction: up to 14,000,000 (of which up to 4,000,000 were fitted on site)
- Number of rivets fitted in an average (10-hour) shift: 200
- Estimated number of workers employed (over the eight-year construction period): 2,320
- Boilers and hydraulic engines: 2 steam pumping engines; 8 large hydraulic engines; 6 x 100 ton accumulators; 4 Lancashire boilers; 8 electric motors of 50 horsepower (hp) each
- Total cost of construction: £1,184,000
- Highest-ever number of bridge lifts in one day: 64

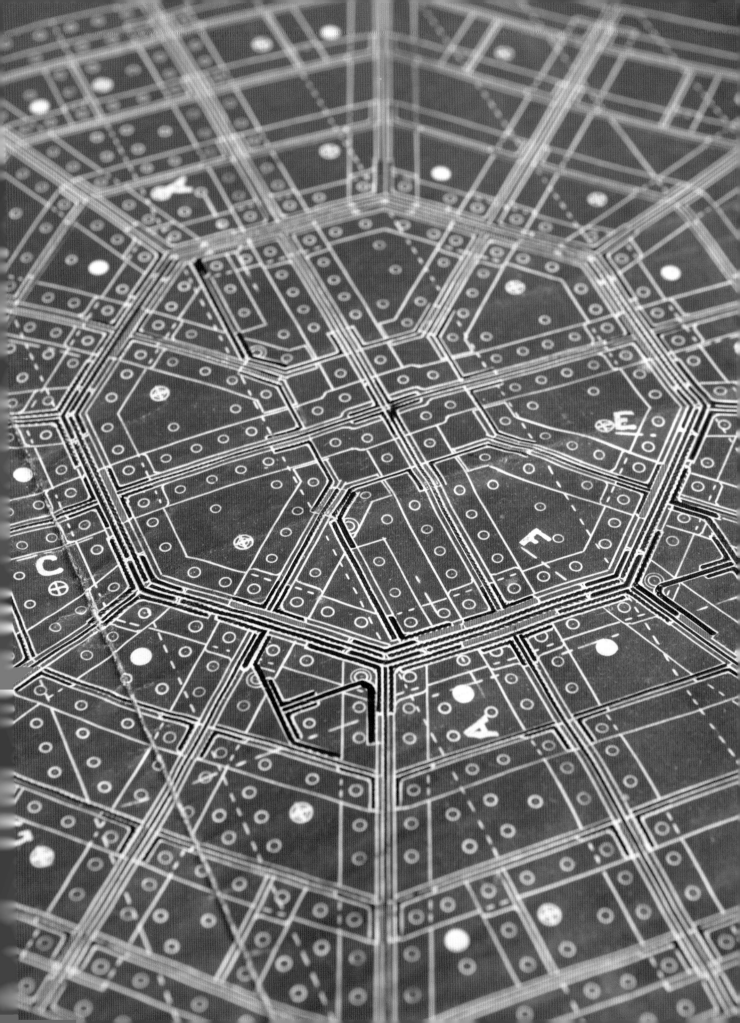

NOTES

CHAPTER 1

1. A. Beresford Pite, 'The architecture of the bridges of London', *RIBA Journal*, xv (14 May 1908), p. 441.
2. Charles Welch, *History of the Tower Bridge and of Other Bridges over the Thames Built by the Corporation of London* (London, 1894), p. 54.
3. Welch (1894), p. 133.
4. Quoted in Welch (1894), pp. 147–48.
5. Report to the Bridge House Estates Committee (1871), quoted in Welch (1894), p. 148.
6. *Ibid.*

CHAPTER 2

1. Cited in Honor Godfrey, *Tower Bridge* (London, 1988), p. 11.
2. George Measom, *The Official Illustrated Guide to the South-Eastern Railway* (London, 1853), p. 4.
3. *The Triumphant Bore: a Celebration of Marc Brunel's Thames Tunnel* (exhibition catalogue, n.d., 1993?), p. 23.
4. J. E. Tuit, *The Tower Bridge: its History and Construction from the Date of the Earliest Project to the Present Time* (London, 1894), p. 18.
5. Welch (1894), pp. 153–54.
6. Tuit (1894), p. 29.
7. *Ibid.*, p. 30.
8. *Ibid.*, p. 31.
9. *Ibid.*, p. 32.
10. Quoted in Godfrey (1988), p. 23.
11. Welch (1894), p. 159.
12. *Ibid.*, p. 161.
13. *Idem.*
14. 'Aquarius', *The Tower (High Level) Bridge: an Imperial Question* (1878), unpaginated copy in Institution of Civil Engineers Library.
15. Welch (1894), p. 164.
16. *Idem.*
17. *Ibid.*, p. 167.
18. *Idem.*
19. *Ibid.*, p. 169.
20. London Metropolitan Archives, CLA/012/01/006, Bridge House Estates Committee minutes.
21. Welch (1894), p. 174.
22. Michael Wheeler, *Ruskin and Environment: The Storm Cloud of the 19th Century* (Manchester, 1995), p. 135.
23. Welch (1894), p. 173.
24. *Idem.*
25. John Wolfe Barry, *Description of the Tower Bridge, Its Design and Construction*, in Welch (1894), p. 218.
26. Welch (1894), p. 182.
27. Godfrey (1988), p. 26.
28. Welch (1894), p. 175.

CHAPTER 3

1. *The Architect* (24 December 1886), quoted in Godfrey (1988), p. 26.
2. Barry in Welch (1894), p. 203.
3. *Ibid.*, p. 185.
4. *Ibid.*, p. 217.
5. *The Graphic* (30 June 1894), quoted in Godfrey (1988).
6. Barry in Welch (1894), p. 193.
7. G. E. Cruttwell, 'Subaquaeous foundations for bridges and docks', lecture to the Institution of Civil Engineers, 1899.
8. Barry in Welch (1894), p. 190.
9. London Metropolitan Archives, Bridge House Estates Committee minutes, May 1888.
10. Barry in Welch (1894), p. 211.
11. Godfrey (1988), p. 25.
12. *Ibid.*, p. 32.
13. Tuit (1894), p. 76.
14. Barry in Welch (1894), p. 209.
15. *The Graphic* (30 June 1894), quoted in Godfrey (1988).
16. Barry in Welch (1894), pp. 205–6.
17. *Ibid.*, p. 206.
18. *Idem.*
19. *Ibid.*, p. 216.
20. Tuit (1894), p. 56.
21. Godfrey (1988), p. 57.
22. *Building News* (29 June 1894).
23. *Building News* (6 July 1894), p. 28.
24. Beresford Pite (1908).

CHAPTER 4

1. London Metropolitan Archives, Bridge House Estates Committee minutes, December 1887.

CHAPTER 5

1. E. T. Cook, *Highways and Byways in London* (London, 1902), pp. 44–45.
2. Trystan Edwards, 'Great Engineers: Sir John Wolfe Barry', *Structural Engineering*, vol. 13, 10 (1925).
3. H. S. Goodhart-Rendel, *How Architecture is Made* (London, 1947), pp. 100–01.
4. Ian Nairn, *Nairn's London* (Harmondsworth, 1966), pp. 122–23.
5. Peter Ackroyd, *London: The Biography* (London, 2000), p. 717.
6. Theo Crosby, *The Necessary Monument* (London, 1970), p. 63.
7. Terry Farrell, *Shaping London: The Patterns and Forms That Make the Metropolis* (Chichester, 2010), p. 56.
8. Ken Allinson, *Architects and Architecture of London* (Oxford, 2008).

CHAPTER 6

1. Information supplied by Tower Bridge staff.
2. *Ibid.*

FURTHER READING AND ARCHIVAL SOURCES

Peter Ackroyd, *Thames: Sacred River* (London, 2007).

Felix Barker and Ralph Hyde, *London as It Might Have Been* (London, 1982).

John Wolfe Barry, *The Tower Bridge: a Lecture* (London, 1894).

Stephen Croad, *London's Bridges* (London, 1983).

Theo Crosby, *The Necessary Monument* (London, 1970).

Dockland: An Illustrated Historical Survey of Life and Work in East London (London, 1986).

Honor Godfrey, *Tower Bridge* (London, 1988).

Henrietta Heald, *William Armstrong: Magician of the North* (Newcastle upon Tyne, 2010).

Nicholas Kenyon (ed.), *The City of London: Architectural Tradition and Innovation in the Square Mile* (London, 2011).

Gustav Milne, *The Port of Roman London* (London, 1983).

Oxford Dictionary of National Biography, articles on 'Sir William Arrol', 'Sir John Wolfe Wolfe Barry', 'Sir John Jackson', 'Sir Horace Jones'.

Patricia Spencer Silver, *Tower Bridge to Babylon: The Life of Sir John Jackson, Civil Engineer* (Sudbury, Suffolk, 2005).

J. E. Tuit, *The Tower Bridge: its History and Construction from the Date of the Earliest Project to the Present Time* (London, 1894).

Charles Welch, *History of the Tower Bridge and of Other Bridges over the Thames Built by the Corporation of London* (London, 1894).

David Wight and Julia Dudkiewicz (eds), *Tower Bridge: A Celebration of 120 Years, 1894–2014* (London, 2014).

Elizabeth Williamson and Nikolaus Pevsner, with Malcolm Tucker, *The Buildings of England: London Docklands* (London, 1998).

The principal source of archival material on Tower Bridge is London Metropolitan Archives, which holds the records of the City of London Corporation and a very extensive collection of ephemera, historic photographs and other visual material. The records of Armstrong, Mitchell & Co. are held at Tyne & Wear Archives in Newcastle upon Tyne. Glasgow City Archives houses the archives of Sir William Arrol & Co., Ltd.

The library of the Institution of Civil Engineers in London is a source for a number of lectures and other papers relating to Tower Bridge. Other material is held in the libraries of the Institution of Mechanical Engineers and the Institution of Structural Engineers.

A collection of drawings by Horace Jones is deposited in the British Architectural Library, Royal Institute of British Architects, London.

ACKNOWLEDGMENTS

This book was commissioned by Tower Bridge in association with Thames & Hudson and I am grateful to Rob Woollard and the team at Tower Bridge, especially Richard Smith, Dirk Bennett and Glen Ellis, for information, advice, guided tours and practical demonstrations of the bridge operation. At Thames & Hudson, Julian Honer and Susannah Lawson provided their customary editorial guidance and support while Jane Cutter has worked her usual magic on the production. Thanks are due to Sophia Gibb for expert picture research, contributing so much to the appearance of the book. Sarah Yates was a truly outstanding editor, patient, supportive and a pleasure to work with. Peter Dawson of Grade Design has been an outstanding collaborator whose vision for the book and attention to detail on every aspect of the layouts have been invaluable.

I am very grateful to Honor McCabe (formerly Godfrey), the author of the excellent 1988 book on Tower Bridge, for sharing information with me and generously loaning me her files. Professor Andrew Saint of The Survey of London, whose knowledge of the capital's history is second to none, provided invaluable advice. The prime source for the history of the bridge is London Metropolitan Archives and I am grateful to the staff there for their usual expert guidance in exploring the great body of material in the archives. The staffs of the libraries of the Institutions of Civil Engineers, Mechanical Engineers and Structural Engineers were generous with their time and advice, as were the staff of the Royal Institute of British Architects.

PICTURE CREDITS

Every effort has been made to trace all copyright holders and to obtain their permission for the use of copyright material and to obtain permissions from those individuals included in documentary photographs. The publisher apologizes for any errors or omissions and shall gratefully receive any corrections. These will be incorporated in future reprints or editions of this book.

LONDON METROPOLITAN ARCHIVES

Many of the images in this book have been provided by London Metropolitan Archives. Free to visit and open to everyone, London Metropolitan Archives cares for historical documents, photographs, films and maps that record the history of London from 1067 to the present day. It is one of the finest and most extensive city archives in the world, and could be described as 'the memory of London'. To find out more visit www.cityoflondon.gov.uk/lma

Key to abbreviations:
a: above; b: below; c: centre; l: left; r: right

Front jacket ©Julian Honer; **back jacket** London Metropolitan Archives, City of London (COL/CCS/PL/01/002/A/302); **2–15** ©Julian Honer; **16** London Metropolitan Archives, City of London (COL/CCS/PL/01/002/A/301); **17** ©Julian Honer; **18–19** London Metropolitan Archives, City of London (Collage 34751); **20al** ©The British Library Board. All Rights Reserved/Bridgeman Images; **20ar** ©Museum of London; **21** ©British Library Board. All Rights Reserved/Bridgeman Images; **22c** ©Museum of London; **22b** London Metropolitan Archives, City of London (Collage 31835); **23** London Metropolitan Archives, City of London (Collage 4412); **24** ©British Library Board. All Rights Reserved/Bridgeman Images; **25** ©Museum of London; **26a** Guildhall Art Gallery, City of London. GLC Heritage Collection (Collage 14155); **26b** Topfoto; **27** Getty Images/photo by London Stereoscopic Company; **28–29** ©PLA Collection/Museum of London; **31a** De Agostini Picture Library/R. Merlo/Bridgeman Images; **31b** Edinburgh University Library, Scotland/by kind permission of the University of Scotland/Bridgeman Images; **32** Getty Images; **33** Topfoto; **34bl** Guildhall Art Gallery, City of London (Collage 11586); **34br** London Metropolitan Archives, City of London (Collage 17453); **35a** Guildhall Art Gallery, City of London (Collage 11448); **35b** London Metropolitan Archives, City of London (Collage 21487); **36a** London Metropolitan Archives, City of London (SC/GL/NOB/B/S3/TOW/BRI c. 1880); **36b** London Metropolitan Archives, City of London (Collage 28205); **37** London Metropolitan Archives, City of London (Collage 34287); **38a** London Metropolitan Archives, City of London (Collage 28196); **38b** London Metropolitan Archives, City of London (Collage 34788); **39** London Metropolitan Archives, City of London (Collage 7399); **40** London Metropolitan Archives, City of London (Collage 22410); **41** By kind permission of The Institution of Civil Engineers, London; **42a** London Metropolitan Archives, City of London (Collage 285805); **42b** Science & Society Picture Library/Getty Images; **43** London Metropolitan Archives, City of London (Collage 237840); **44a** Universal Images Group/Getty Images; **44b** Getty Images; **45a** *The Engineer*, vol. 82 (30 Oct 1896), p. 448/by kind permission of The Institution of Civil Engineers, London; **45b** *Illustrated London News* (9 April 1870); **46** London Metropolitan Archives, City of London (COL/SVD/PL/03/0271); **47a** London Metropolitan Archives, City of London (SC/GL/NOB/B/S3/TOW/BRI 1876); **47b** London Metropolitan Archives, City of London (Collage 22768); **48–49** London Metropolitan Archives, City of London. Wakefield Collection (Collage 28165); **50** London Metropolitan Archives, City of London (Collage 28211); **51a, c, b** *The Engineer*, vol. 76 (15 Dec 1893), p. 545/by kind permission of The Institution of Civil Engineers, London; **52** *The Tower Bridge* by J. E. Tuit (1894), p. 23; **53a** London Metropolitan Archives, City of London. Purchased with aid from the NACF and the MGC/V&A Purchase Grant Fund in 1999; **53c** London Metropolitan Archives, City of London (Collage 34445); **54** Guildhall Art Gallery, City of London. Bequeathed by the sitter's daughter Miss A. H. Jones, 1969 (Collage 11920); **56a** London Metropolitan Archives, City of London (Collage 318434); **56b** London Metropolitan Archives, City of London (Collage 1206, **57** ©Julian Honer; **58** Science & Society Picture Library/Getty Images; **59** *The Tower Bridge* by J. E. Tuit (1894), p. 29; **60c** *The Tower Bridge* by J. E. Tuit (1894), p. 25a; **60b** *The Tower Bridge* by J. E. Tuit (1894), p. 27; **61** *The Tower Bridge* by J. E. Tuit (1894), p. 25b; **62a** London Metropolitan Archives, City of London (COL/SVD/PL/03/0294); **62b** London Metropolitan Archives, City of London (COL/SVD/PL/03/0293); **63** Tower Bridge Visual Records; **64** Private Collection/Photo ©Gavin Graham Gallery, London/Bridgeman Images; **65** Science & Society Picture Library; **66** London Metropolitan Archives, City of London (Collage 2053); **67** Mary Evans Picture Library; **68** Topfoto; **69al** Courtesy of the Brunel Institute – a collaboration of the SS Great Britain Trust and the University of Bristol; **69ar** Mary Evans Picture Library; **70–71** Look and Learn/Peter Jackson Collection/Bridgeman Images; **73a** Library of Congress/Print & Photographs Online Catalogue (Reproduction No. LC-DIG-ppmsca-00861); **73b** London Metropolitan Archives, City of London. Chadwyck-Healey Collection (Collage 17911); **75** *Minutes of Proceedings of The Institution of Civil Engineers Vol CXXVII Session 1896–7 Part 1*/by kind permission of The Institution of Civil Engineers, London; **76–77** *The Tower Bridge* by J. E. Tuit (1894), p. 35; **78–79** London Metropolitan Archives, City of London (COL/PL/01/176/B/013); **80a** *The Engineer*, vol. 76 (15 Dec 1893), fig. 45/by kind permission of The Institution of Civil Engineers, London; **80b** By kind permission of The Institution of Civil Engineers, London; **81bl** New York Daily News Archive/Getty Images; **81br** Mary Evans Picture Library/The National Archives, London, England; **82** London Metropolitan Archives, City of London. Tower Bridge Construction Collection (Collage 323341); **83** Topfoto; **84al (no. 1)** By kind permission of The Institution of Civil Engineers, London; **84ar (no. 2)** London Metropolitan Archives, City of London. Tower Bridge Construction Collection (Collage 323335); **84cl (no. 3)** London Metropolitan Archives. Tower Bridge Construction Collection (Collage 323344); **84cr (no. 4)** London Metropolitan Archives, City of London. Tower Bridge Construction Collection (Collage 323353); **84bl (no. 5)** London Metropolitan Archives, City of London. Tower Bridge Construction Collection (Collage 323343); **84br (no. 6)** London Metropolitan Archives, City of London. Tower Bridge Construction Collection (Collage 323355); **85al (no. 7)** London Metropolitan Archives, City of London. Tower Bridge Construction Collection (Collage 323351); **85ar (no. 8)** London Metropolitan Archives, City of London Tower Bridge Construction Collection (Collage 323350); **85cl (no. 9)** London Metropolitan Archives, City of London. Tower Bridge Construction Collection (Collage 323360); **85cr (no. 10)** London Metropolitan Archives, City of London. Tower Bridge Construction Collection (Collage 323375); **85bl (no. 11)** London Metropolitan Archives, City of London. Tower Bridge Construction Collection (Collage 323365); **85br (no. 12)** London Metropolitan Archives, City of London. Tower Bridge Construction Collection (Collage 323346); **86a** *The Engineer*, vol. 76

(15 Dec 1893), p. 558/by kind permission of The Institution of Civil Engineers, London; **86b** *The Engineer*, vol. 76 (15 Dec 1893), p. 574/by kind permission of The Institution of Civil Engineers, London; **87** By kind permission of the Institution of Civil Engineers, London; **88** By kind permission of the Institution of Civil Engineers Scotland Museum; **89a** Topfoto; **89b** *The Engineer*, vol. 89 (18 May 1900), p. 507/by kind permission of The Institution of Civil Engineers, London; **90a** London Metropolitan Archives, City of London. Tower Bridge Construction Collection (Collage 323353); **90b** SC 562092/©Courtesy of Historic Environment Scotland (Sir William Arrol Collection); **92** London Metropolitan Archives, City of London. Tower Bridge Construction Collection (Collage 323342); **93** *St James's Budget 29 June 1894*, Shelfmark MFM.MLD32/The British Library; **94bl** ©*Illustrated London News*/Mary Evans; **94br** London Metropolitan Archives, City of London. Tower Bridge Construction Collection (Collage 323339); **95a** London Metropolitan Archives, City of London. Tower Bridge Construction Collection (Collage 323368); **95b** London Metropolitan Archives, City of London. Tower Bridge Construction Collection (Collage 323380); **96** London Metropolitan Archives, City of London (COL/CCS/PL/01/002/A/301); **97** London Metropolitan Archives, City of London (COL/CCS/PL/01/002/A/302); **98** London Metropolitan Archives, City of London (COL/CCS/PL/01/002/A/307); **99** London Metropolitan Archives, City of London (COL/CCS/PL/01/002/A/312); **100–101** London Metropolitan Archives, City of London (COL/CCS/PL/01/002/A/313); **102** William Sugg History Archive; **103** London Metropolitan Archives, City of London. Tower Bridge Construction Collection (Collage 323355); **104–5** London Metropolitan Archives, City of London. Tower Bridge Construction Collection (Collage 323366); **106** London Metropolitan Archives, City of London. Tower Bridge Construction Collection (Collage 323362); **107** ©The British Library Board. All Rights Reserved/Bridgeman Images; **108** London Metropolitan Archives, City of London (Civic Entertainments 1894); **109** Guildhall Art Gallery, City of London (Collage 11801); **110** London Metropolitan Archives, City of London (COL/SVD/PL/10/0321); **111al** ©Museum of London; **111ar** London Metropolitan Archives, City of London (SC/GL/NOB/C/048/4); **112–13** Tower Bridge Visual Records; **114** By Courtesy of the Brunel Institute – a collaboration of the SS Great Britain Trust and the University of Bristol; **115** akg-images; **116bl** National Trust Photographic Library/Bridgeman Images; **116br** ©*Illustrated London News*/Mary Evans; **117bl, br** ©Julian Honer; **118a** London Metropolitan Archives, City of London. Tower Bridge Construction Collection (Collage 323363); **118b** London Metropolitan Archives, City of London. Tower Bridge Construction Collection (Collage 323364); **119** ©Julian Honer; **120–21** Tyne & Wear Archives; **122** Tower Bridge Visual Records; **123–24** ©Julian Honer; **125** Grade Design; **126–27** Illustration by Grade Design based on an original created and devised by Jam Creative and Bright; **128** Topfoto; **129a, b** ©Julian Honer; **130** ©Julian Honer; **131bl, br** By kind permission of the Institution of Civil Engineers, London; **132** Topfoto; **133** Science & Society Picture Library; **134–35** ©Museum of London; **136–39** ©Julian Honer; **141** All images ©Al Overdrive; **142–43** ©Julian Honer; **144al** Mary Evans/Grenville Collins Postcard Collection; **144ar** ©Julian Honer; **144b** This Life Pictures/Alamy; **145** Heritage Images/Getty Images; **146–47** ©PLA Collection/Museum of London; **148a** London Metropolitan Archives, City of London (Collage 36717). (By kind permission of the Commissioner of the City of London Police); **148b** London Metropolitan Archives, City of London (Tower Bridge uncatalogued collection B08/167); **149al** Barratts/S&G Barratts/EMPICS/PA Images; **149ar** ©PLA Collection/Museum of London; **150** Courtesy John Laing Construction; **151** Matthew Lloyd/Getty Images; **152–53** ©Julian Honer; **154a, b** Corbis Historical/Getty Images; **155** ©Julian Honer; **156bl** David South/Alamy; **156br** Steve Vidler/Mauritius Images GmbH/Alamy Stock Photo; **157** Waring Abbott/Michael Ochs Archives/Getty Images; **159a** P Floyd/Hulton Archive/Getty Images; **159b** ©Julian Honer; **160** Matt Gibson/MGB2211615/Superstock; **162–63** ©Clive Totman; **165** Photo by Mansell/The LIFE Picture Collection/Getty Images; **166** ©UPPA/Photoshot; **167** Photo by O. Louis Mazzatenta/National Geographic/Getty Images; **168–70** Photos by George Pickow/Three Lions/Getty Images; **171** Topfoto; **172–73** Tower Bridge Visual Records. Courtesy, and with kind permission, of the family descendants; **174–75** Photo by George Konig/Keystone Features/Getty Images; **176** Photo by George Pickow/Three Lions/Getty Images; **177** Daily Mail/Solo Syndication; **178** Hulton Archive/Getty Images; **179** Photo by George Pickow/Three Lions/Getty Images; **180–81** PA Images; **183** ©Julian Honer; **192** ©Julian Honer.

CAPTIONS FOR PAGES 2–17, 183 AND 192:

2–3: The MS *Hamburg* enters the Pool of London through Tower Bridge.

4: Detail of original machinery located on the south side of the bridge.

6–7: A view looking east across the River Thames and Tower Bridge.

8: The south tower.

9: Detail of the suspension steelwork on the east side.

10–11: Blueprint diagram and detail of one of the four original coal-fired boilers.

12: Part of the original machinery, located on the south side of the bridge.

13: Control panels and dials inside the south-east cabin.

14–15: One of the huge subterranean chambers into which a bascule slides when the bridge is opened.

16: Elevation drawing by G. D. Stevenson of one of the towers facing the bridge opening section.

17: The south tower and high-level walkways.

183: As this blueprint of the steelwork indicates, the precise locations of all 14,000,000 rivets were carefully planned.

192: The east side of Tower Bridge and the adjacent warehouses (now apartments) of Butler's Wharf, viewed from the north bank of the River Thames.

INDEX

First published in the United Kingdom in 2019 by Thames & Hudson Ltd,
181A High Holborn, London WC1V 7QX

Tower Bridge: History • Engineering • Design © 2019 Thames & Hudson Ltd, London

Text © 2019 Tower Bridge on behalf of the City of London Corporation
Text written by Kenneth Powell

Designed by Peter Dawson, gradedesign.com

British Library Cataloguing-in-Publication Data
A catalogue record for this book is available from the British Library

ISBN 978-0-500-343494

Printed and bound in China by Asia Pacific Offset Ltd

To find out about all our publications, please visit **www.thamesandhudson.com**.
There you can subscribe to our e-newsletter, browse or download our current catalogue,
and buy any titles that are in print.